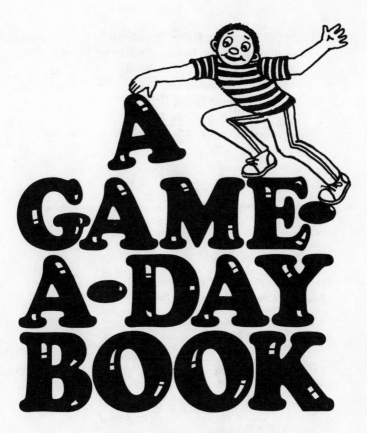

A GAME-A-DAY BOOK

Gyles Brandreth

Illustrated by Lucy Robinson

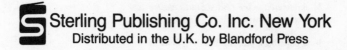Sterling Publishing Co. Inc. New York
Distributed in the U.K. by Blandford Press

Books by Gyles Brandreth
The Biggest Tongue Twister Book in the World
A Game-A-Day Book
A Joke-A-Day Book
Seeing Is Not Believing
Super Joke Book
Writing Secret Codes and Sending Hidden Messages

Library of Congress Cataloging in Publication Data

Brandreth, Gyles Daubeney, 1948–
   A game-a-day book.

   1. Games—Juvenile literature   I. Robinson
Lucy.   II Title.
GV1203.B677   794   80-91386
ISBN 0-8069-4610-5
ISBN 0-8069-4611-3 (lib. bdg.)

ISBN 0-8069-7878-3 paper

ANT LANGUAGE

Start the year by learning to speak a new language—in minutes! Just put the word "ant" in front of every vowel or pair of vowels. (Vowels are the letters a, e, i, o, and u.) So "Now begin" becomes "Nantow bantegantin," "Hello" becomes "Hantellanto" and "Goodbye" becomes "Gantoodbyante." If you can persuade someone else to learn the same language, you can hold a private conversation—even when other people are listening.

2

HAPPY NEW YEAR!

It may be too cold to do much outside on this second day of the year, so let's just wish our family, friends and visitors a very happy new year on a tin-can telephone. Here's how:

Find two clean, empty cans which have no sharp edges or anything likely to cause injury. Get a good supply of strong thin string.

Now, punch a small hole in the middle of the bottom of each can, using a hammer and nail. Thread each end of the string through the bottom of a can and tie several knots, one on top of the other, to keep the ends in place inside the cans. You now have two tin-can earphones and mikes. When the string is pulled taut you can talk into one can and the other person can hear the message in the other can. Now set up the telephone so the sender and receiver cannot see each other, and make sure the string *is very taut and does not touch anything between the cans*. Remember to say "Over" at the end of each message to stop two people from talking at the same time.

TIN CAN SHY

Start by making six beanbags (these make the best missiles).
Cut out twelve pieces of fabric about 5 × 4 inches (12 × 10
cm) each, and sew them together in pairs, sewing all around
the edges. Before closing the fourth side of each pair, fill half
the bag with dried beans or peas.

Now find six thick sticks about 4 feet (120 cm) long and six
empty soda cans. Push the sticks into the ground about 2 feet
(60 cm) apart, and balance a can on each one.

Each competitor stands on a base line 10 feet (3 m) away
and scores one point for each can knocked down with a bean-
bag. Let everyone have at least 3 turns at throwing all six bags
before totaling up to see who has the highest score.

4

BUSTING THE TAPE

This is the time for New Year's resolutions, so here is something that you could aim to keep up all year round. Boys will
probably want to "bust the tape" more than girls, but breathing deeply every morning is good for everyone.

Breathe in deeply and measure your chest with a lightweight tape measure to get a maximum reading. Then breathe
out and take a minimum reading. The difference between
the readings tells you how much your chest has expanded.
You can keep a note of your progress every day to see how
much your chest has expanded over the year.

One day you may even bust the tape and they'll call you
"Buster."

PUSH THE CORK

Mark out a *short* course for this race (say, about 20 feet [6 m] long) so the players won't collapse exhausted before they reach the finish. Each player has an ordinary bottle cork and has to crawl along on all fours, pushing it along with his nose, trying to be the first to reach the finish line.

6

SNOW PEOPLE

Holding a personality parade for snow people is far more fun than making an ordinary snowman. Personalities can be men, women, cartoon characters, animals, birds—anything!

Working with a friend, or alone, use wooden or plastic kitchen spatulas to shape the features. Three feet (1 m) high would be a good size to aim at. Dress the finished figures in old shoes, hats, scarves, glasses. The odder the snow personalities look, the better.

GOOGLY BALLOON

For this game you need one more balloon than there are players—so if there are five players you need six balloons. Before you blow the balloons up, push a marble down through the neck of each one. You will find this makes the balloons bounce in all kinds of directions.

The aim of the game is to keep all the balloons in the air at the same time, using heads only. Hands are definitely out! No one wins this game, but everyone has a good time playing it.

8

FREEZE

Despite its title, this game has little to do with cold January weather. It can be played whenever the weather is good enough for you to be out-of-doors.

One player must place a handkerchief in his or her back pocket and stand at one end of a playing field with his back to the other players who are widely scattered within a distance of about 200 feet (60 m) from him. One of the players gives the signal to start. The players now have to approach the one out in front as quietly as they can. Without any warning, the lone player can turn around quickly and point to any player who is making a move at that moment and send him out of the game.

The trick is for the players to keep their eyes on the one in the front all the time and to freeze the second he makes a move. The first player to snatch the handkerchief hanging from the front player's back pocket wins.

GUESSING GAMES

Prepare six different games, then ask your family or friends to play them. Keep a note of all the guesses and award two points to the person nearest to the right answer in each case. Here are some ideas of what to prepare:

1. A bowl of water—how many teaspoonsful?
2. A ball of wool—how many feet (meters)?
3. An eggcup full of rice—how many grains?
4. A child's bucket full of stones—how much does it weigh?
5. An envelope full of paper clips—how many paper clips?
6. A closed book—how many pages?

10

HUMAN PARCEL

For this game you need two teams of two or three people each, plus two very willing volunteers.

Using newspaper, wrapping paper, Scotch tape and string, or any packing materials at hand, make a parcel of the victim which *might* be accepted at any post office, or by a railroad for delivery. Be sure to leave openings at the nose and mouth so your package can breathe.

When it comes to judging the winner, the prize goes to the neatest-wrapped parcel.

B-GONE

Here are ten words which once contained the letter B. Some of them even had more than one B. The remaining letters have been shuffled. Can you guess the words?

1. urett
2. relu
3. toa
4. ule
5. ste
6. hati
7. lal
8. oc
9. tie
10. ketnal

(Answers start on page 183)

12

TELEPHONE NUMBERS

If you feel in need of a quiet five minutes, why not sit down with a friend or two and try working out mnemonics, or memory aids, for each other's telephone numbers.

Suppose your number is 765-4723. Your friends could simply remember 7-3-5 and take it from there. How? Seven is the first digit and also the fifth. The next three digits add up to 15 which is 5×3. The last two digits add up to 5 and the last digit is 3.

Now try your friends' numbers.

TRIPOD FOOTBALL

Build a tripod of heavy sticks to act as a goal. (The sticks simply rest against each other at the top and are not tied.) Players now form a large circle around the goal and aim to kick a ball and knock down the tripod. Either take turns at kicking, or do so when the ball comes your way. Count a point for each knockdown a player makes.

After ten minutes, see who has scored the most points.

14

BROOMSTICKS

With practice, this game will quickly become a favorite. For each player you need a broomstick, or any kind of stick about 5 feet (150 cm) long.

The players should stand in a circle roughly 3 feet (90 cm) away from each other, each holding a broomstick in front of them with both hands, its end on the floor. At the word "Now!" from a spectator, each player lets go of his stick and moves quickly to the right to try and catch his neighbor's before it hits the ground. Every player is allowed three falls of the stick before he or she is out.

After a little practice the players will be able to stand up to 2 yards (2 m) apart.

Another idea is to shout "Right!" or "Left!" instead of "Now!" so that the players are uncertain which direction they will have to run in until they hear the spectator call it out.

FOURTEEN ALL

Play this patience game with an ordinary pack of playing cards. Shuffle them, remove the top 4 cards and put them aside.

Now, set out 16 cards in 4 rows of 4. Look at the cards and cover every pair that totals 14 points with a face-down card. (Jack=11, Queen=12, King=13, Ace=1.)

Next, deal a face-up card onto every card that has not been covered. Once more look for pairs totalling 14 points and cover them with face-down cards.

Keep pairing, covering and dealing as long as you can. The aim is to end up with all 16 original cards covered with face-down cards before the pack is used up.

16

CRAFTSMAN KIM

Kim's game can be played in hundreds of ways. You need a tray prepared in advance (for Craftsman Kim it should carry a selection of home handyman's tools) and covered with a cloth. The cloth is removed for one minute and then replaced. Players must then write down a list of all the things on the tray they can remember.

There are numerous variations of this game. The tray can carry about 24 related or unrelated objects (related ones are easier to recall). It could have small kitchen utensils, desk items, small toys, or even several dominoes. In this case, you would have to remember the numbers showing on the dominoes, e.g. one 5:6, two 4:4, and so on. This must surely be the hardest variation of all.

The winner is the player who has remembered the most correct items.

ISLAND SHAPES

Draw the shapes of several different islands of the world on colored craft paper, cut them out, and mount them on large sheets of white paper. Scale is unimportant: it is the shape that counts. Hand out pencils and paper and see who can name the most islands correctly.

18

SNOW CASTLE

Compete with a friend or, if there are more than two of you, work in pairs.

Place a large square of hardboard or cardboard on a cleared patch of snow and work quickly to build your castle on it.

Wear warm woollen gloves with rubber kitchen gloves on top and use plastic or wooden spatulas as tools to build the castle of your imagination.

Call in a neutral judge to say who wins with the most attractive castle.

SHADOW PLAY

Try this game on a dark winter evening. All you need is a plain white and a bright table lamp or flashlight. Put your hands between the lamp and the wall so that they throw shadows and see how many recognizable animal shapes you can make.

20

THE TOUCH GAME

This is a good game to try out on just one friend. You must each go around the house with a large bag, collecting a lot of different objects such as hair brushes, combs, toothbrushes, a magnifying glass, a desk paperweight, a pair of binoculars, a hammer, a small attaché case, a bar of soap, or even sea shells if you have a collection.

Now blindfold your friend and see if he or she can guess your objects one at a time by feeling them. Then it is your turn to guess your friend's objects. If that is too easy, wear thick gloves when you are guessing.

MUSICAL
NUMBERS

It's surprising how often numbers occur in song lyrics. For a real laugh, get everyone to sit down and rack their brains and, if possible, sing a line or two.

There's *Just One More Kiss, One More for the Road, Tea for Two, In Eleven More Months and Ten More Days I'll be Out of the Calaboose*, and *When Two's Ideal Then Three's a Crowd*. How many more songs can you find that have numbers in the title? If you get stuck, try looking through some old sheet music for inspiration.

Set a total to beat, and keep a running total of all the numbers—the group above comes to 30—to see who wins.

22

SPLIT WORDS

Try this quick brain teaser. Here are eleven words that have been split into groups of three letters. Can you put the groups back together again to find the words?

TRY	HIT	CHO	EDY
NET	ODY	RHY	OOL
RGY	POE	RCH	HEA
AMP	PRI	MAG	MEL
THM	CHU	ENE	EST
COM	SCH	RUS	TER

(Answers start on page 183.)

HOW MANY NOTES?

For this game you need a piano and someone who can play it—a little bit at least. Ask the pianist to play a few bars of a very simple tune, using one hand only. Ask him or her to repeat it with everyone listening intently. How many notes did he play?

It is unlikely you will have two answers the same in a room full of people!

Play the tune again, very slowly indeed, and work it out.

If the audience gets very good at this game, let the pianist cover his hand with a handkerchief—and then try again.

24

FETCH

For this game, everyone sits down on the ground with a volunteer "leader" in front. He or she is not allowed to say a word, but mimes an object he would like brought to him—a glass of water, perhaps, or some checkers, a biscuit, or a balloon. He then points to one of the players to bring the object. When the correct object has been fetched and put in front of the "leader," it is the turn of the one who brought it to ask someone else to fetch!

SKIPPING GAMES

Lots of active games can be played while skipping. Try:

1. skipping follow the leader
2. a skipping relace race
3. skipping musical chairs
4. a skipping marathon.

Can you think of more variations?

26

FIND THE TREES

Can you find these hidden trees?

1. The metal describing the tree must appear,
   So a two-word answer is needed here.

2. It's a hedge that might spoil the view,
   In a way it's written here for you!

3. Symbol of the Lebanon this tree,
   There very well cared for . . . maybe.

4. The Palm tree will change you'll find,
   If you tuck the letter E behind. . . .

5. To offer a branch of this tree,
   Used to mean "Peace it shall be."

6. What an oarsman might well do,
   Starts the tree: add letters two!

7. There is a Wych variety
   Of this very common tree.

(Answers start on page 183.)

WOLF, WOLF . . .

Play this in a darkened room to make it more scary. One player is the wolf, the others are the sheep. The wolf calls out loudly: "Sheep, sheep, come over here." "No," shout the sheep, "the wolf is near." "No," shouts the wolf, "he's gone to . . . ." (fill in any city), "and won't be home tonight."

At this, the sheep try to cross the room to the other side. The wolf leaps out and "devours" (by tapping) whatever sheep he can catch, and the other sheep turn tail and run back. Then it starts all over again until just one sheep is left. He then becomes the wolf.

28

INDIAN BOWLS

Northern tribes of American Indians had a favorite game called the "Bowl Game" and later "Indian Bowls." Here is an adaptation of it. Collect as many peach stones as you can, dry them and smooth them on sandpaper. Paint one side of each in a bright color and let them dry.

Divide the stones between two boxes and divide the players into two teams, each member also holding a small box. The idea is for one person in each team to throw their box of peach stones into the air and for the other players in the team to catch as many as possible in their own boxes. Any stone caught counts one point. Any stone caught colored side up, counts a bonus point.

One team plays at a time to avoid collision. The winning team is the one with the most points.

THUD AND BLUNDER

This is a lively game to play with two teams. Each team stands at opposite ends of a room. There is a mat or small piece of the carpet on the floor by their feet, and each team has one or more beanbags between them.

The object of the game is to score goals against the opposite team. You do this by landing your beanbags on their mat. So, at the word "go," the beanbags are thrown backwards and forwards, as both teams aim for the opposite mat and try to defend their own at the same time.

It is best to set a time limit on this game. The team with the most goals in 3 minutes is the winner.

30

BARK RUBBINGS

It is possible to identify trees from rubbings of their bark. Try some rubbings yourself, but collect a leaf or two to go with each one so that you can be sure to identify them later. (Never take the bark off a living tree, for that would expose it to attack by insects and disease.)

Use thin paper and a wax crayon held on its side. Hold the paper firmly against the bark, or take it in place, and rub gently with the wax until the design appears.

Make a collection of different tree rubbings, keeping track for yourself what tree each rubbing is from. Then see how many trees your friends can identify from your collection.

RIDING THE TRAINS

This game is not competitive but it is a lot of fun!

Get a group of your friends together and choose one of them to be the engine—one of the old-fashioned steam engines. The others are going to be the extra passenger and freight cars. The engine shunts backwards and forwards, picking up the rest of the train. The others join on behind him, one at a time. You couple onto the train by putting one hand around the waist of the person in front, so you can pick up all kinds of freight with your free hand, like boxes or bags or even a small stool.

The whole train can only move backwards and forwards, so it takes some time to pick up all the waiting cars. Everybody joins in with the sound effects as they go.

1

TABLE TENNIS RELAY

Divide the players into two teams and give each team a table tennis paddle and ball.

At the word "Go," the first player in each team sets off holding the paddle at arm's length, with the ball balanced on it. She must run to the other end of the room and back before passing the paddle to the next team member. If the ball is dropped, that player must go back to start and begin again. Of course, the ball may *not* be held on the paddle.

An easier variation is to run the race while tapping the ball up in the air on the bat.

The team whose players finish first is the winner.

2

GHOSTLY ENCOUNTER

Candlemas Day, February 2, comes halfway between the shortest day of the year and the spring equinox, when the hours of light and darkness are equal. Mark this day by playing a game by candlelight.

You need a polished round table and 26 index cards, each with a letter of the alphabet marked on it. Lay the cards around the edge of the table and put a glass tumbler upside down in the middle.

Everyone sits around the table with his or her right forefinger resting lightly on the tumbler. Then someone asks: "Is there anyone there?" The tumbler will probably move slightly and spell out "Y-E-S." You can now continue, asking the "ghost" questions that can be answered with just one word. The answers could be gibberish—but you never know!

CHALK MARKS

In order to avoid letting this game get too rough, it should be limited to no more than five players on each side.

You need two wooden boxes, painted black, one at each end of the room. Each team is positioned around its own half of the room. At the word "Go," the umpire throws a piece of white chalk into the middle of the room. A goal is scored by chalking a mark on the other team's black box, and the game then starts again.

Limit play to three minutes a set. The winning team is the one that "chalked" the most marks.

4

"MANNERLY" QUIZ

How many words of four or more letters can you make from the word MANNERLY?

(Answers start on page 183.)

5

AGATHA'S BELL

St. Agatha is the patron saint of bellfounders and bellringers and February 5 is the day when Roman Catholics in many parts of the world ring out bells in her honor. Bread, in the shape of a bell, is often baked to celebrate St. Agatha's Day as well.

Here's a hearing game for which you need a small handbell or toy with a bell inside it. Blindfold a volunteer and then shake or ring the bell at varying distances away. The blindfolded person has to guess how far away the bell is each time. This is much more difficult than you probably think.

6   **February**

QUARTER
STAFFS

Quarter staffs is probably one of the oldest games in the world. All you need is a pair of heavy sticks, preferably ash or some similar hard, strong wood. They should be about four feet (120 cm) long, free of rough edges and any sharp pieces. Opponents face each other, holding the sticks firmly with both hands near the ends. The game is started by crossing the sticks against each other at right angles.

Now starts a trial of strength. Using feints, half-moves, or any ploy while still holding the stick with both hands, each player has to try to outmaneuver the other, until one is forced to the ground or drops his stick. For best results, try to match the players in height and weight.

7

THE CAT GAME

Take turns with your friends asking a "cat" question. For example, you might ask: "What kind of cat killed Goliath?" Answer: a CATapult. Or: "What kind of cat makes a very long list?" Answer: a CATalogue.

Score a point if you ask a question no one can answer. Anyone who cannot think of another "cat" question when his turn comes is out. Total up each player's points when you finish the game to see who wins.

ACTING STRANGELY

Players must all sit in a circle. The first player starts with an action—clapping his or her hands twice, perhaps. The next player copies this action and adds one of his own—he might nod his head. The third player copies these two, then makes up something himself. And so it goes on. Anyone who makes a mistake or cannot think up something new is out. The winner will be acting very strangely.

9

BOOK RELAYS

This team game can be very funny to watch.

Divide players into two teams, with the same number of players in each team. Each player puts a book on his or her head and makes his way around a set course—across the room, around a chair, over a stool, under a pole propped across two chairs, and so on. One player goes around the course at a time.

Every time a book is dropped, that player loses two points and goes back to the start and begins again. Touching the book with your hands loses four points for the team. A clear round scores six.

Set a five minute time limit and have an umpire/timekeeper for each team. When all players have made a round of the course, count up all plus and minus points for each team to see which team wins with the highest score.

PAIRS

Prepare this game ahead of time—it makes a very good party opener. Collect a number of things that are usually thought of together—for example, cup and saucer, fork and spoon, nut and bolt, holly and ivy, needle and thread. Wrap them all up separately and then, when the time comes, give one parcel to each player. The winning pair is the first to find its other half.

11

THE EDISON GAME

Thomas Alva Edison was one of American's greatest inventors. He was born on February 11, 1847. See how inventive you can be, and make as many words as you can from the letters of his name. The words can have any number of letters in them.

BIRTHDAY LUCKY NUMBERS

Abraham Lincoln was born on February 12, 1809. Do you know what his lucky number was? To find it, you add the numbers of the month, the day and the year: $2 + 1 + 2 + 1 + 8 + 0 + 9 = 23$. Now add the two digits and you get $2 + 3 = 5$, his lucky number.

Now that you know how to do it, you can work out your own lucky number and those of your friends.

13

FIGURE-EIGHT RACE

Draw out a very large figure eight in chalk on a playground or sidewalk. Make marks across it, about 3 feet (1 m) apart. Label one of them "start" and then number the rest. Now, gather together six players, three bicycles and three dice. The players work in pairs, one of them on a bike, the other in charge of the dice.

All riders begin at start, and their partners take turns at throwing the dice and calling out the numbers. The riders then move forward that number of places.

The winning pair is the one with the first rider to go around the figure eight three times, finishing at "start."

VALENTINO

If you are giving a party on Valentine's Day, you can all have fun writing your own Valentine messages. Write down the name of famous personalities and put them into a hat. Everyone draws a name and becomes that person for a while. They must now write a Valentine to the person their new name might be attached to, making it as funny as they like.

Results naturally have to be read out loud.

PROVERBS

Here are the key words from ten proverbs. Can you guess what they all are?

1. Jack
2. time
3. light
4. last
5. crying
6. rolling
7. gone
8. cloud
9. words
10. policy

(Answers start on page 183.)

CRAFTY

Play this game in groups of three or four. Each group has a box containing identical items—colored papers, Scotch tape, pins, paper clips, felt pens, lengths of old curtain material, raffia, wood, pieces of felt. Each group must make something, *anything*, from the materials provided and has an hour to do it in. Award a prize to the group with the most attractive creation.

17

THE LIE DETECTOR

Play Lie Detector to see how good you are at making people believe what you tell them. You must stand up and give an account of your life—when and where you were born, where you went to school, how many pets you have had, where you have been on vacation . . . Is it all true? Your friends must watch you closely and see if they can detect anything that isn't true. Perhaps you will blush and give the game away, or look away from their gaze, or stutter. . . . Can you defeat the lie detectors?

If a player challenges something you say and is wrong, he or she is out of the game. If his challenge is correct, you become one of the lie detectors and the challenger becomes the storyteller.

TAKE A CARD

Try this game at home with the family one evening. Write the letters of the alphabet on pieces of cardboard and ask everyone to take one. You each now have fifteen minutes in which to produce as many articles as you can find beginning with the letter you have drawn.

You score one point for every article you find. If you have drawn a Q or Z, you score two points for each article. The person with the highest score wins.

19

AUTOGRAPH

Try this game to set everyone at ease at the start of a party.

Tack (or tape) a very large sheet of white paper on a well lit wall or board and have a soft-tip pen ready.

Now ask everyone to autograph the paper. They must write with their usual hand, but at the same time swing the opposite leg around in a circle in a clockwise direction.

You will be surprised how difficult this is to do and what fun it is to watch.

BODY NAMES

Some people's last names are connected to parts of the body. Can you think of seven? Here are some to start you off: Head, Hart, Kneebone, Winterbottom.

If you can't think of any more names right off, try a race with a friend with each of you using a telephone directory to see who can come up with the most names in ten minutes.

21

TALKING PICTURES

Search around for old advertisements that have large pictures of people's heads on them. Mount them on firm cardboard, and cut out the faces from the pictures. You can now put your own face behind the hole in one picture, a friend behind another, then carry on a conversation with the picture alongside you.

You could do this by way of entertainment at a family party. The room can be in darkness until a spotlight outlines what appear to be two fine old pictures side by side. The cross-talk between the faces of today in the costumes of yesterday must be well prepared, and it is best to concentrate on everyday topics.

THE OPERATION

Try this just for fun as a way of entertaining your friends.

First set up a large white screen (used for home movies) with a table just behind it. Gather together a bright table lamp or flashlight and an assortment of strange objects. Get a volunteer to lie down on the table and set the light shining on the screen so that when you hold up an object the light casts a clear shadow on the screen.

You can now pretend to carry out an operation in shadow play. Pretend to cut a large slit in the volunteer's middle and remove all sorts of bits and pieces from it. Don't forget to sew the patient up when you have finished!

23

DOG IN A MANGER

This is a very old game which was played by children in many parts of Europe during the 16th century. Collect an assortment of pebbles, stones, shells, driftwood, flotsam and jetsam, fir cones, acorns, woodland debris, or any other small objects you can lay your hands on. Indoors you could collect objects such as dominoes and small toys.

Mark out a circle for the Manger and put the objects inside it. (Mark the circle with rope on a lawn, with chalk on a wood floor, or with a line drawn in the sand on a beach.) Choose one player to be the Dog. The rest of the players have to try and steal an item of treasure from the Manger by approaching stealthily, feinting, stopping and staring and finally snatching something in a lightning pounce. If the Dog touches a player, then he or she is out. Mass pounces are strictly forbidden.

DOWN, DOG, DOWN!!

Be careful not to be too rough playing this game. You will win by using your strength skillfully, not by going wild!

Two players stand facing each other with arms raised high. Each player interlocks his fingers strongly with the player opposite, and at a given signal they begin to push the other hard, using only the fingers. This means they must press down hard on their opponent, trying to force him down to his knees. The successful player shouts: "Down, Dog, Down!!"

25

MAILMEN

Cut up some large plastic bags so that you end up with several large plastic rings like the one in the illustration. These are the mailbags, and you will need three bags per player.

Divide the players into two teams: Mailmen and Bandits. Each Mailman puts a mailbag over his shoulder and, at a given signal, the Bandits break loose and try to pull at the bags until they break. Each Mailman may return to base twice for another mailbag before he is out of the game.

The winner is the Bandit with the most mailbags to his credit. Then the teams can change roles and start again.

Just to make it more difficult, you could play this game on roller skates, as they do in Sweden.

AMERICAN STATES

Can you solve these anagrams quickly? Each one is an American state.

1. A Cool Rod
2. Africa Lion
3. "Ah! Ma, Look!"
4. And Eva . . .
5. "Anna? Tom?"

6. China Mig
7. Hal is on a court
8. Hand soldier
9. "I'm Ena!"

(Answers start on page 183.)

27

PANCAKE CONTEST

Shrove Tuesday is the day before Ash Wednesday, the first day of Lent, which culminates in the Christian festival of Easter. Since Easter is a "movable festival," the date of Shrove Tuesday varies too, but it usually falls in late February. Traditionally, the larders were cleared of luxuries such as eggs, fats and sugar on Shrove Tuesday, and these were turned into pancakes.

See if you can get all your friends and neighbors to join in a pancake race. Each participant needs a frying pan with a pancake in it. Mark out the course, and add a few obstacles—something to jump over, a rope to crawl under. Everyone must toss his or her pancake three times enroute, catching it safely in the pan. If a player's pancake falls on the ground instead of in the pan, he or she must start again at the beginning.

WHEN WE WERE YOUNG. . . .

Ideal for a family gathering, this game is sure to bring back lots of memories. Ask all the guests to bring with them a photograph of themselves when they were young (the 3-5 year age range is best). Cover a table with a paper and lay all the photographs on it, writing a number beside each one.

Before the guests begin to leave, write the correct name beneath each photograph, so that all mysteries will be solved.

29 (in a leap year)

JUMPING JOHNNY

Find a bag with a drawcord top and put a pair of slippers or a scarf inside it before tying it to the end of a long rope. This is the Johnny. The filling needs to be soft, yet heavy enough to make a weight that can be swung around.

Take turns standing in the middle of the play area and swing the Johnny around in a circle just a few inches (centimeters) off the ground. The other players must jump, jump and jump again as the Johnny comes around and keep a note of the number of times they are hit by it. After everyone has had a turn with the Johnny, find the winner by seeing who has scored the lowest number of hits.

HOT SHOT

For this game you need a small piece of heavy wood about 5 inches square and ¾ inch thick. Draw a large circle about 6 feet (2 m) in diameter on the ground with a small circle, about 3 feet (1 m) in diameter, in the middle of it. Put the wooden block in the middle.

The players stand around the outer circle and, with a tennis ball, try to knock the wooden block out of the inner circle.

The nearest player on the other side of the circle fields the ball and tries to knock the wood himself. One point is scored each time the wood is knocked out of the circle. Play for ten minutes to see who is the best shot.

2

CENTIPEDES

Play this game in teams of four or five. Players in each team should squat down, one behind the other, arms around the waist of the person in front. Now practice bobbing up and down in unison, and when you can do that, try hopping along in step. When you think you have mastered this, challenge another "centipede" to a race.

METALLIC NAMES

How many last names can you think of that are connected with metals? Easy "metallic" names are Gold, Silver and Steel. Then there are Goldsmith, Silverman, Leadbetter, Ironside and Copperfield. Try this as a team game and pool your ideas.

4

SPROUTS

This is a game invented by two mathematicians, but you can play it quite easily yourselves. All you need is a pencil and a good-sized piece of paper.

First, draw three or four dots anywhere on the paper. The first player then draws a line between two of the dots or starts and finishes in a loop from a single dot. Having drawn his line, he makes a new dot somewhere along it. Now the next player has a turn and does exactly the same thing. As the paper is passed around, the players draw more and more lines, but none of them must ever cross and no dot must have more than three lines coming from it.

The winner is the last player who is able to draw a line.

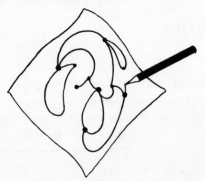

VOLLEY BALLOON

Push a glass marble or smooth pebble through the neck of a balloon before blowing it up to give you a "ball" that is difficult to control. Mark out a play area about 25 by 15 feet (7.5 × 4.5 m), or smaller if you don't have the space, and tie a rope across the middle at a height of about 6 feet (2 m).

Divide into two teams of five players each and stand on opposite sides of the net. The "ball" is hit backwards and forwards across the net. Each team tries to hit the "ball" down onto the ground within the playing area on their opponents' side. If they manage this, they score a point, but if the "ball" goes out of the playing area, they lose a point. You can hit the "ball" as many times as you like among the members of your own team before hitting it over the net.

The first team to reach seven points wins.

6

WRISTY

This game of strength has many different names. Lie down flat on your stomach, facing your opponent. Both of you place right elbows on the ground and grasp hands very firmly. At a given signal, you must try to force your opponent's hand down until the back of it touches the ground. Whoever does this is the winner, so long as the elbows of both players have remained on the ground at all times. If they haven't, the game starts again until you get a fair result.

STRAIGHT FACE

Who can keep a straight face when someone else is making silly faces? Try it.

Make as many faces as you like—cross your eyes, giggle, wrinkle your nose, stick out your tongue, wiggle your ears, and so on. The person watching you must keep a straight face while looking you in the eye the whole time.

Now switch roles. The person to remain straight-faced longest is the winner.

8

RUNNING THE GAUNTLET

Imagine a U.S. Navy ship running the gauntlet through narrow straits to safer waters. You need two well-defined lines down the room, making a channel not more than 10 feet (3 m) wide. The ship is one team linked together by holding a rope. The other team mans the banks, armed with balls of balled-up newspaper. At a given signal the lights go out, and in "dead of night," the ship attempts to run the gauntlet. There is a flash of lightning as the lights are switched on for a moment and the ship is attacked by a barrage of newspaper balls, most of which are sure to miss. Unless everyone can claim a direct hit, the ship can keep on its course and sail to and fro until it is sunk.

ANIMAL EMBLEMS

Which countries do these animals represent?

1. Bald-headed eagle
2. Lion
3. Kiwi
4. Beaver
5. Kangaroo
6. Elephant
7. White leghorn cockerel
8. Black bull
9. Springbok
10. Bear

(Answers start on page 183.)

10

HEAVE-
HEAVE-
HO!

Most simple games of strength depend on pushing and shoving techniques, but here's one that depends on pulling.

Two players sit on the ground facing each other, the soles of their bare feet pressing against each other. Their hands are flat on the ground on either side of them. At a given signal the contestants take their hands off the ground and grasp hands firmly.

They take the strain, and then start pulling as if they were in a rowing boat. The winner is the player who can make his opponent lift his seat off the ground with a sudden strong, hard pull.

DODG'EM

Dodg'em is a game of variety, since the players move from one form of contact to another.

Start by having two players face each other, with arms out straight and fists clenched tightly. The knuckles of each pair of hands should be just touching each other. The players try to outstare each other without laughing or saying anything, and then one player tries to rap lightly the knuckles of his or her opponent. If the player succeeds, he or she scores a point, but if he fails his opponent wins the point. After five points have been scored by either player, the game changes; elbows are the target, and later shoulders. Then count up the score to find a winner.

12

LOST PERSON

This game is a good one for testing everyone's powers of observation.

If you are giving a party, ask a neighbor to visit while the games are in progress. The visitor should come into the room, mutter something, and if possible, cross the room and leave by another door.

About half an hour later ask your friends to give a description of the intruder.

Quite probably, many of the descriptions will be very different and some people will not have seen anyone at all!

13  **March**

BEWARE POISON!

Place a cardboard box on the floor. It contains a very deadly poison—an imaginary one, of course. All the players must gather around it in a circle, holding hands tightly. At the word "Go," the game starts in earnest, with everyone pulling against everyone else, but still keeping the hand grasps intact.

If any players touch the box of deadly poison, or a hand grasp fails, then they are out. Make sure it's not you, but try and make either of your immediate partners the victims.

The circle must always be over and around the poison. Eventually there will be only two players left and there will be quite a contest!

14

ANIMAL CRIES

The more players you have for this game, the better. Split the players into five or six teams, each with a leader, and name each team after an animal—cat, dog, horse, donkey, sheep, cow. Scatter some dried beans (about five per player) all over the floor and shout "Go." Team members have to find a bean, cover it with their foot, and then make the noise of their particular animal until their leader comes to pick it up. Only the leaders may touch the beans with their hands. When a player has had his or her bean collected, he can go off and find another one. The noise has to be heard to be believed! The winning team is the one whose leader has the most beans.

TABOO

The aim of this game is to avoid using a particular letter of the alphabet. Any number of people may play.

One player is the question master. He or she decides which letter is taboo and then asks the players questions in turn. They must answer in phrases that make sense and do not contain the forbidden letter. Anyone who uses the letter is out, and the last remaining player eventually becomes the next question master.

16

THE MEMORY GAME

The memory game can be played by eight or more players, but the more people who join in, the better it is.

Send one player out of the room for a couple of minutes. During this time the rest of the players must sit on the floor in any way they like, some cross-legged, some feet out, some staring upwards into space, others at the ground. Some may face the other way leaning on their elbows, others with their faces cupped in their hands, and so on.

Call the first player back and let him look closely at the others for one minute only. He must then go out again for one minute, during which time two players must change places and postures. When the observer comes in a second time, he must name the players who have moved.

If more than eight people are playing, send two or three observers out of the room and get twice as many players to change position as there are observers.

"EMERALD" QUIZ

Today is St. Patrick's Day, for the patron saint of Ireland, which is also known as the "Emerald" Isle. To be topical, see how many words of four letters or more you can make from the word "Emerald."

(Answers start on page 183.)

18

SIDE BY SIDE

Play this game in a large playground or in a hall where you are allowed to chalk on the floor.

Draw two lines about the width of six people apart, and about 30 feet (10 meters) long, to make a "road." You now need four volunteers who will be blindfolded and placed back to back in pairs to act as "watchmen" at two points along the road.

The rest of the players must see if they can get from one end of the road to the other without being heard and pointed at by the watchmen. This is best done on tiptoe and side by side in pairs, splitting up to move around the watchmen.

See how many times you can go up and down the road while remaining undetected.

COLORFUL SONGBIRDS

These American songbirds have a color as part of their name. Can you guess them?

1. — headed woodpecker
2. — finch
3. — bird
4. — jay
5. — winged blackbird
6. — eagle
7. — bird

(Answers start on page 183.)

20

NEWSREADER

See how much your friends can remember about the front page of a newspaper. Give each one a copy of the same edition of the same paper and allow them four minutes to study it.

Collect the papers, hand out writing paper and pencils, and ask six questions. The answers should all be found on the front page the players have read.

Make a note of the scores and try again with page two, this time changing places with one of the players.

Continue until everyone has had a turn as question master.

CATCH!

It looks easy! It *is* easy! But it isn't as easy as all that. Two players must stand facing each other. One has his or her arms stretched out in front at shoulder height, with hands not less than 6 inches (15 cm) apart. The other holds an empty matchbox or cigarette packet between the first person's hands. Now the game can start.

The player holding the box suddenly drops it without warning. The other player must try to catch it before it reaches the ground. Easy? Just try! The player with outstretched arms will try to trap the box between the palms of the hands, but there are easier ways to do it. The other player can build up suspense by delaying the drop.

22

WHO'LL GET THERE FIRST?

In this game for two players, each must have an identical street map. An umpire calls out the name of a street and the players see who will be the first to pinpoint it on the map and so gain a point. The first player to reach five points is the winner.

If your maps have street finder indexes, be sure to cover them up before you start playing.

HOW MANY COINS?

Tell your audience that you can not only tell their ages but also find out how many coins they have in their pockets.

Ask for a volunteer and ask him to double his age, add 5, and multiply by 50. Now he must add the number of coins in his pocket (if there are none, he adds nothing), and tell you the total.

All you have to do is deduct 250. You will be left with four figures. The first two are the person's age, the second two the number of coins he has.

24

BALLOON BALL

For Balloon Ball you need two teams of five players each and a good supply of balloons. Stretch a rope about 4 feet (120 cm) off the ground across a small playing area and ask each team to stand on either side of it.

The umpire throws a balloon into the middle to start. Players must keep the balloon off the ground on their own side and try to tap it down to the ground on their opponents' side. You use only your head, body, and legs. You can kick the balloon but you cannot use your hands or arms below the elbow.

Whenever the balloon touches the ground, a point is awarded to the other side. The same happens if any player catches hold of it. A burst balloon is replaced by the umpire who throws the new one into the middle.

Play until one team has 11 points—or until the balloons are all burst.

HAMBURGERS, BEANS AND FRENCH FRIES

Try this just for a laugh. Take turns with a friend reading a story aloud, but read "hamburgers" instead of any word beginning with an "h," "beans" instead of words beginning with "b," and "french fries" instead of words beginning with "f." Score a minus point every time you forget to substitute.

Each player should read the same story aloud. When you're finished, count up to see who has the fewer minus points.

26

BARRICADES

Clear a large room and build barricades of furniture here and there, with a major obstacle right across the middle. (This need not be more than knee height.) The whole of this barricaded area is Forbidden Territory. It is divided into four quarters and a blindfolded Guard is set on the sideline to listen intently.

Players must cross the Territory in twos and threes from one end to the other in the absolute quiet of night maneuvers. The moment a Guard hears a sound, he or she must point immediately to the trespasser. Anyone who is caught is out. Let everyone have a try at crossing and then select a new Guard.

ALL KINDS OF EGGS

Which are the eggs that make you cry out?
Exclamations (eggs-clamations) of course!
Which are the eggs which take you on an outing?
Excursion (eggs-cursion).

  See if you can solve the questions below. The answers all begin with "ex," but we're pronouncing it as "eggs."

1. Which are the eggs that make you breathe out?
2. Which are the eggs that give an apology?
3. Which are the eggs given out by a car engine?
4. Which are the eggs that explain in detail?
5. Which are the eggs that are always outside?
6. Which are the eggs overflowing with high spirits?
7. Which are the eggs putting on a public display?
8. Which are the eggs that hurry things along?

(Answers start on page 183.)

28

BALANCING THE BOOKS

Stretch out a long narrow ribbon or a piece of string along the floor and weight it with a book at each end. Now put three books on your head and walk along the line, arms stretched out to the sides. Can you get to the end of the string without dropping the books?

  Let everyone have a try. Those who were successful try again with four books. Add an extra book each time to find the champion.

  Needless to say, if the onlookers see any foot stray from the line, that person is out.

STRANGE COUNTRIES

The names of these countries are not really as foreign as they look. It is simply that the letters have been jumbled up. If you have a second hand on your watch, time yourself to see how quickly you can sort them out, then challenge a friend to beat your record.

1. Cocomor
2. Adini
3. Yonraw
4. Danielc
5. Voluiyagas
6. Bazzarin
7. Dhalitan
8. Nagah

(Answers start on page 183.)

30

BALLOON RACES

Have you ever taken part in a charity balloon race? You buy a helium-filled balloon (helium is much lighter than air) and write your name and address on a special printed label. Eventually the card may be mailed back to you and you will see how many miles it has traveled.

You can try this with ordinary air-filled balloons and a package of tie-on labels. Stick a postage stamp on each label and write a note to the finder asking him to write on the label where it was found and to mail it back to you. Launch the balloons from a hill on a windy day.

They won't go hundreds of miles, but you might be surprised how far they do travel.

HARE AND HOUND

Put everyone's name into a hat and pick two out. The first
player drawn is the Hound. She must be blindfolded and given
a small can containing a few coins or stones. The second
player is the Hare. He is also blindfolded, but given a tightly
rolled-up newspaper. Everyone else can stand or sit anywhere
they like in the room.

The Hare must set off, in whichever direction he likes,
rattling his can quite often. The Hound must pursue the Hare
and whack him lightly with the newspaper when she finds
him. No help is allowed from the watchers, even when the
players come within inches (centimeters) of each other.

After a while, let two others have a go at it.

ALL CHANGE!

This is an April Fool's game to play on the family—but get permission from an adult before doing it!

When everyone is out, set to work in the dining room or living room and change the position of ten things. You could move a table or chair, or even take one away completely. Move the pictures around, hide the ashtray, and so on. One way or another, make ten changes, some obvious, some less than obvious.

When the family comes home, wait until someone notices. You will be surprised how long it may take. Then see if anyone can list all ten changes.

2

FLYING PLATES

This game is best played in a hall with a wooden floor. You need two teams of three players each, and three paper plates.

Draw a circle about 4 feet (120 cm) in diameter at the other end of the room from the players. Each member of the first team must try to slide a plate into the circle. Only plates *completely* over the line will count, and score as follows: 1 plate = 1 point, 2 plates = 4 points, 3 plates = 10 points.

Then let the second team take its turn.

For a variation, try sliding the plates by pushing them off with your feet instead of by hand.

MODERN NURSERY RHYMES

Try this game for a few laughs at a party. Ask everyone to make up a modern version of a nursery rhyme, starting with the original first line. Finish these first, to get the hang of it, then off you go with more of your own.

"Little Jack Horner,
Went into a sauna"

"Mary had a little lamb,
Her mother *was* surprised!"

"Georgie-Porgie, pudding and pie,
Came home from school with a big, black eye "

Award a prize for the funniest rhyme.

4

KICK STICK

The Zuñi Indians of North America loved a game which in their own language they called Kick Stick. This is an adaptation of it.

Mark out a large figure eight on the ground. Starting at the crossing point of the eight, try to kick a short, heavy stick all around the figure from start to finish without letting the stick lose contact with the line once. If you *do* lose contact with the line, start again at the beginning.

Play this on your own as a game of patience, or take turns with a patient friend.

STONE AGE

Play this game where there are lots of stones. Push a heavy stick upright into the ground so it stands about a foot (30 cm) above the ground. Balance a large stone on top of it.

Now everyone stands 3 feet (1 meter) back (not in a circle, though!) and has three throws with small pebbles to try to hit the stone. One point is awarded for each hit.

For the next round everyone stands a yard (1 m) farther back, and on each new round, stands a few more feet (meters) back.

The player who has scored the most hits by the time you finish is the winner.

6

FINGERPRINTS

Can you recognize fingerprints? Could you even recognize one of your own if you saw it on paper? The answer is probably "No." Make a game of it. Take the right index finger only of every player and imprint each one on a white index card, using ink from an ordinary rubber stamp pad. Using your own personal code, mark each card on the reverse side so that you can identify the fingerprint's owner later.

Mix all the cards up and let the players try to identify their own prints. They could be at it all night! Finally, put them out of their suspense and decode your identifying marks.

Now let them study their own print under a magnifying glass so that they will have better luck next time.

TREASURE MAP

Draw an imaginary island and mark on it all the pirate symbols you can think of . . . skull and crossbones, gold ingots, kegs of rum, barrels of flour, muskets and so on. Also mark an X—the spot where the buried treasure is lying waiting to be discovered.

Let everybody have a very good look at the map of the island, for about three minutes. Then take it away. Each player must now re-draw that island from memory—its shape and everything marked on it! Would anyone's map have led him to the treasure?

8

THREE-WAY TUG

This is a great game for three people of equal size. Make a rope circle by tying the two ends of a rope into a firm square knot and fixing the two loose ends of rope to the main circle with adhesive or surgical tape. Lay the circle on the floor and space out three tennis balls around it, each one about 6 feet (2 m) from the rope.

The three people must now pick up the rope circle and, holding it firmly in one hand, try to pick up a ball with the other. As all three will be pulling in different directions, this is much more difficult than it sounds.

9

THE
RAFT
GAME

Why not try a game of musical chairs without any chairs. Lay several old pages of newspapers in the middle of the room to make a "raft" large enough for everyone playing to stand on.

Now put on some music while everyone "swims" around the raft, and remove one of the newspaper pages. As soon as the music stops, the players must try to get onto the raft. Those who cannot are "drowned."

Eventually there will be a tiny raft in the form of one newspaper page. The first person aboard this must make sure there is no room for anyone else.

10

I WENT SHOPPING

How good is your memory? Test it in a game with one or more friends. You start by saying, "I went shopping and I bought . . ." and then add anything you like—perhaps "a big pack of bubblegum." The next person repeats your item, then adds his or her own—perhaps "a pair of sneakers." The next player does the same, and so on. Any player who forgets an item or puts them in the wrong order, is out.

To make things more difficult, the items you buy could be real tongue-twisters, like "seven hand-sewn silk shirts." Continue adding items to your list until all but one player have made mistakes and gone out of the game. The one remaining player is the Memory King or Queen.

JOURNEY OF TERROR

Everyone must play this game in bare or stockinged feet and players take turns making the journey in alphabetical order of last names.

The first victim stands ready while the other players sit down in two lines facing each other, legs out straight and feet touching. Hands must be flat on the ground at their sides.

The first player sets off between the two lines, stepping over the feet—if possible—while the others move their feet about and do their best to trip her up. If she makes it through without falling, she goes back for another round.

12

EASTER BONNET

It is surprising just what can be done with a newspaper and a safety pin. Hand these items out to each of the players and give them five minutes to make an Easter bonnet.

If you prefer, you can play this game in pairs, with one person acting as the model and the other as the milliner.

13

RISE AND SHINE!

Sit down on the ground, facing an opponent, legs straight out, knees on the ground, and the soles of your shoes pressing firmly against each other. Now reach forward and grasp each other firmly around the wrists. You must each pull and try to lever the other person up and off the ground. Can you make him or her rise and shine?

BEARS

If you are giving a party, this game is sure to break the ice.

Put a bun on a plate in the middle of the floor and ask the players to stand around it in a large circle. Then say that you are going to whisper the name of an animal to each person in turn. Do this, making sure no one overhears what you tell another. Now announce that you will call the name of an animal and that person must grab the bun before you count three. Now shout out "Bear," and everyone grabs at the bun, because you gave everyone the same animal name! Their laughter is sure to break down any shyness.

15

HIDDEN TREES

This game requires you to do some advance work in preparing clues before the other players arrive. The names of local species of trees must be worked into sentences or statements of fact and the list of sentences pinned on the wall. Each player has a pencil and paper to jot down the names of the trees he or she can find in the sentences.

An example of the kind of sentence needed is: "*If I r*eceive a proper invitation, then I'll be there." The answer is, of course, "fir."

Whoever finds the most hidden trees is the winner.

16

HIDDEN NOTES

Here are the initial letters of twelve proverbs. For example,
S i g = Silence is golden. Can you work out what the proverbs are? When you have done them, try them on your friends.

1. A w p n b
2. A r s g n m
3. P i g h s t s
4. F b c
5. I t e b t c t w
6. A m t h g f
7. T m c s t b
8. A s i t s n
9. M h m l w
10. H a l i b t n
11. A m i a g a a m

(Answers start on page 183.)

17

A MAGIC ARM

Tell a friend you can make him raise his arm, even against his will. He will naturally ask you to prove it.

Get him to stand alongside a wall, then have him stretch out his arm, close his fist, and press against the wall as hard as possible. After a minute, ask him to move away from the wall and put his arm down by his side. Now say a magic word and watch what happens to his arm. It will automatically rise up a little.

GEM SMUGGLERS

See if you can spot the precious stones hidden in these sentences by splitting the words up differently, e.g. RUB Your eyes and take another look—RUBY.

1. As you said, I am on duty today.
2. Please stop all that noise.
3. Get up early if you want to come too.
4. It is no use shutting a gate when the horse has bolted.
5. To make strawberry jam, berries and sugar are boiled together.

(Answers start on page 183.)

19

NOSEY

How keen is your sense of smell? Can you distinguish the smell of burning fabrics from that of paper? Do you know the smell of burning wood? Do you know the smells of *different* woods burning—apple tree logs, or cherry wood, or pear tree?

Collect specimens of burnt objects and store them in small airtight screw-topped jars. You will find they retain their characteristic smells a very long time this way. Then you can play Nosey, asking your friends to identify the smells of burning materials as a quiz game.

DESERT ISLAND

This simple but energetic game is a variety of old-fashioned hoop wrestling. Play it by using a large bicycle tire as a circle, or chalk a circle on a wooden floor and announce it is a desert island.

You are the sole occupant of the circle, and defy anyone else to push you off it and take possession. Only arms and bodies may be used—no legs or feet—and the contest must be strictly one against one. The occupier of the circle is out as soon as a foot is placed outside the circle. The best of three games decides the winner.

21

LIST OF FIRSTS

The first signs of life, when spring takes over from winter, are usually easily recognizable. Many trees flower in February, particularly the witch hazel with its catkins. The blackbird and songthrush are the first birds to sing, and the first baby animals to be born are usually rabbits. Look, too, for the first flowers and even, if you are lucky, the first butterfly. Make a list of twenty "firsts" you can see for this year.

COMPASS KAREN

Start by drawing a large chalk circle on the ground or by marking one out with a stick on a beach.

Cut the circle in half with a line drawn from north to south across it. Draw a second line from east to west. Then draw a line down the middle of each quarter to make eight segments. Label them according to the eight points of the compass.

Place an object in each segment and allow everyone one minute to memorize them before you cover them all up. Now the players must write down their answers, e.g. glove at north, hat at north-east, etc.

If this is too easy, divide the circle again to give 16 points of the compass. You could even try Compass Karen using all 32 points.

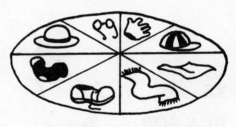

23

GROUP NAMES

A group of sheep is called a flock and a group of fish is called a school. Can you link up these animals with their groups?

1. Bees	A. Litter
2. Cattle	B. Pride
3. Ants	C. School
4. Geese	D. Pack
5. Dogs	E. Gaggle
6. Lions	F. Herd
7. Porpoises	G. Swarm
8. Puppies	H. Colony

(Answers start on page 183.)

TRAMPS' RACE

Mark off an outdoor race course wide enough for all players. Each player must collect five items of old clothing and put them in a pile at the starting point. When the starter blows the whistle, each competitor picks up one item and puts it on, on top of the clothes he is wearing, while running to the end of the course and back to the start. He then picks up and puts on another item, and so on. . . .

The winner is the player to finish the race first, with all five pieces of old clothing on.

25

RUN FOR YOUR LIFE

If you can run very fast while keeping your wits about you, you should do well at this game. You need a tennis ball, a small paddle, and a stopwatch or a watch with a second hand.

One player holds the paddle and the others stand around him in a large circle, one of them holding the ball. The tennis ball is thrown lightly at the legs and feet (below the knee only) of the paddler, who must move very fast around the circle, defending his legs and trying to hit the ball out so as to gain time.

The first person to score a hit takes over the paddle.

The winner is the paddler who lasts the longest.

CHEESE ROLLERS

Every April in England there takes place a traditional cheese-rolling contest in the famous village of Stilton in Cambridgeshire. Stilton cheeses are taken to the top of gentle green hills and rolled off down the slopes. The cheeses which roll the longest distance under their own momentum are the winners!

This is a fun game when you're out in the country. All *you* have to do is find a nearby hill, a collection of old car and truck tires or garbage can lids, and do the same thing as the cheese rollers.

27

JOUSTING

In order to make it quite fair, this game needs a good deal of organization before you start. First, divide the players into two teams, then ask the people in each team to pair off to make a Knight and his Charger. Arrange the Chargers in order of weight, from the heaviest up.

The two teams now line up facing each other in their pairs, the heaviest Chargers at opposite ends of the line. As their number is called, two Knights gallop down between the lines to try to unseat the other rider. Time their fight before calling the next number.

The winning team is not necessarily the one that unseats the most Knights, but the one whose three shortest times add up to less than the others.

ABBREVIATIONS

Here are some of the more common abbreviations you are likely to come across. Do you know what they all mean? Some even have two or more meanings.

1. advt.
2. bart.
3. chem.
4. diam.
5. Gk.
6. M.
7. p.m.
8. R.S.V.P.

(Answers start on page 183.)

29

KNEE RELAYS

Play this as a team relay game. The first player from each team puts a book between his knees and rushes off around the room (one clockwise, one counterclockwise). A dropped book means going back to the start. Hands may be used only during a changeover from one player to another within a team.

Try the game with a big, heavy book and then with a slim, light paperback. Which is easier?

The team that finishes first wins.

30

BRAIN-TEASER

Can you use the ten digits—0, 1, 2, 3, 4, 5, 6, 7, 8 and 9—to form a sum that will add up to 100? Give yourself a paper and pencil and five minutes to figure it out.

(Answers start on page 183.)

ALPHABETICAL SENTENCES

Have a contest to see which player can write down the longest sentence with words beginning with each letter of the alphabet. Score 1 point for each word.

So: "After Bedtime Certain Dogs Eat Fresh Greens Hungrily."—Scores 8.

And: "Artful Boxer Calls Deadly Enemy For Great Hullabaloo In Jelly King's Lonely Mansion Near Old Pretty Quiet Retreat Somewhere Trendy."—Scores 20.

Can you or your friends do better?

2

BLIND SPIDER

Tie several ropes to a beam or a strong branch of a tree. Ask one player to be the spider and wear a blindfold. He or she, and all the other players who are the flies, must hold the end of a rope with one hand. Anyone who lets go is "out"—unless it is the spider, who must be "re-connected."

When the game starts, the spider tries to "swat" as many flies as possible by tagging them with the other hand. They may dodge as they wish, at the same time avoiding getting tangled up in the web-like ropes.

Once a fly has been swatted, he must drop out. The spider wins when all the flies are out. Then the person who survived the longest becomes the next spider and the game begins again.

3

SPRINT TUG-OF-WAR

For this game, you need a playing field with a boundary line at each end and a marked central point. Tie a red marker flag to one end of a rope and a blue marker flag to the other end and lay the rope out in the middle of the field.

Divide the players into reds and blues and send them off to opposite boundary lines. When the whistle is blown, players have to sprint to the rope, pick up their end, and pull it back over their own boundary line. A win is scored as soon as any part of the rope crosses the line.

4

CRAZY HOCKEY

Next time you are out for a walk, look for a good strong stick with a curve at the end, like a hockey stick, and bring it back for a game of crazy hockey.

Draw two parallel lines along the play area, about 20 yards (18 m) long and 1 yard (3 m) apart. Mark a base line, and then 15 yards (13.5 m) from it mark a series of lines across the parallels, at right angles to them, to make "boxes." Number each box. Now find a flat smooth stone, put it on the base line, and see if you can whack it into the box with the highest number. Compete with a friend to see who can score the highest with three hits.

JUMBLED NAMES

You would expect to find all these things in the garden shed, but the letters have been jumbled up. Can you sort them out?

1. WEHLWOERBRA
2. GAWCINTNEAR
3. TOREFWOLP
4. PESDA
5. TOLWRE
6. MELRWAWON
7. LILKEEDWRE
8. TWHESORAE

(Answers start on page 183.)

6

ROPE HORSESHOES

For a rope horseshoe you need a piece of rope about 18 inches (45 cm) long. Fray out the two ends and interweave them to form the rope into a ring, then bind the join with thin string.

Hammer a wooden stake into the ground and make a series of marks from it on the ground at 1-foot (30-cm) intervals. Throw the horseshoe from each mark, and add up your score—one point at the 1-foot (30-cm) mark, two points at the 2-foot (60-cm) mark, etc. The horseshoe must fall right over the stake and lie flat on the ground before you can score.

Now challenge your friends to a game.

FLYING SAUCERS

Make sure you have plenty of outdoor space for this game, so there will be no risk of anyone getting hurt.

Use a Frisbee or just a simple plastic plate. Throw it discus style from a base line and see just how far it will fly before touching the ground (only the first bounce counts). Write your name on a popsicle stick and push it into the ground where your plate fell.

Now throw again, trying to beat your own record, or take turns with friends to see whose throw travels the farthest.

8

THE TRAVEL GAME

This game can be played by any number of players, anywhere, anytime. It makes an especially good game for when you are traveling.

You need two small boxes, one containing cards on which you have written the letters of the alphabet, and one containing cards with different themes—such as Summer Camp, Fire Station, Christmas, Thanksgiving Day, Greyhound Bus, Railroad Station, Filling Station, Sedan, Candy Store, Swimming Pool, Airport, and so on.

One person draws a card from each box and everyone then writes down as many words as they can think of which are connected with the given theme, and beginning with the letter of the alphabet marked on the other card. Give everyone a set time limit, say 5 minutes, and then compare answers. Continue with another set of cards, and so on.

SEEK THE SEVENS

How quickly can you do this puzzle?

Look at the word or words in the left column. In the right column you will find their synonyms—words with the same meaning—but with the letters mixed up. Can you sort them out?

Less expensive	her cape
Defraud	new lids
Strain	in notes
Spring flower	clip sow
Pamper	idle gnu
Colorful spectacle	get a pan
Devotees	cats did

(Answers start on page 183.)

10

CHINESE WRESTLING

Play this game on a firm rubber mat if you've got one. Mark a line in tape across the mat, and bend down, back to back with a friend, on either side of the line. Now, grasp your partner's hands between the legs. If you prefer, you can use one hand only, so that the other is free to support you on the ground. Now start pulling. Whoever pulls the other over the line first is the winner.

This is a test of balance as well as strength but it is best to play with a friend who is similar in size and weight.

AMERICAS' QUICK QUIZ

Trace a large outline map of North and South America and make ten little numbered flags out of paper and pins. Pin the flags on the map and ask ten questions related to where you place them.
Examples:
Flag 1. Name this important Canadian city.
Flag 2. What is the name of this very long river?
Flag 3. What is the capital of this country?

12

SILHOUETTE PORTRAITS

Prepare this quiet guessing game in advance by looking through newspapers and magazines for sideview photographs of famous people. Trace these profiles carefully, and color them in with black before pinning them all on a large sheet of white paper.

When the time comes to start the game, hand out papers and pencils, then sit back and wait to see how many of your friends can guess who the faces are.

13

CART HORSES

Play this game outdoors on grass or sand. First scrape a line clearly on the ground and ask two contestants to stand back to back, one on either side of it, about 6 feet (2 m) apart. Tie the players together with a rope loosely around the waist of each and ask them to kneel on the floor.

Which cart horse is the stronger and will pull the other one over the line when you say "Go"?

AIR, EARTH AND WATER

Players sit in a circle and one is chosen to start. He throws a small ball to any of the other players, calls out "Air" or "Earth" or "Water," and immediately counts to ten as quickly as he can.

If he calls "Air," the player must name a bird or any other thing living in the air. If he calls "Earth," a creature living on the earth must be named. If he calls "Water," the player must name a creature living in the sea, ponds, lakes or rivers. The player naming the creature has to do so before the questioner counts to ten. If he does not, that player is out. Of course, no creature may be named twice.

The game continues with the second player throwing the ball to another player, and may continue until only two players remain.

15

THE WHEELBARROW

Play this game in pairs. One person is the gardener and the other is the wheelbarrow. The gardener grips the wheelbarrow firmly around the thighs above the knees after the wheelbarrow has dropped flat on the grass face down. The wheelbarrow must now stand up on his or her hands and the pair is ready to go.

The gardener is only allowed to push and go forward. The wheelbarrow must squirm and twist about, doing his best to go in any direction except the one the gardener wants!

The wheelbarrow generally wins this game, so everyone should have a turn in both roles.

PATIENCE IN PAIRS

Write the numbers 1 through 20 twice on a sheet of paper, scattering them about on the paper anywhere you like. Draw a line joining two number 1's. Now draw a line joining two 2's, then two 3's. None of the lines is allowed to cross any of the others or go through any of the numbers. See how many pairs of numbers you can join, starting at 1. Then have another go at it, trying to beat your own record.

17

SEVEN MATCH TRICK

Give a box of used matches to a friend and ask him or her to pile them into three heaps on the table. Each heap must contain *not less than three matches* and each heap must also contain the same number of matches.

You, as Mr. or Ms. Magic, can now show your skills: You will promise to make your friend finish with seven matches in the middle heap after only five moves. Learn the routine exactly like this:

1. Ask him to take three matches from the left-hand heap and place them on the middle heap.

2. Now he must take three matches from the right-hand heap and place them on the middle heap also.

3. He must now count the number of matches left in the left-hand heap. Whatever this number is, take the same number of matches from the middle heap and place them on the right-hand heap.

4. Now he must take one match only from the middle heap and place it on the left-hand heap.

5. Then he must take one match only from the middle heap and place it on the right-hand heap.

Now tell him to count the number of matches in the middle heap. It is SEVEN!

DICTIONARY DEFINITIONS

Some of the ordinary objects you use every day sound almost unrecognizable if you read their dictionary definition. For example, a "shallow circular vessel from which food is eaten" is a plate. Can you recognize these other things?

1. "Hard or soft, inflated or solid sphere used in games."
2. "Light circular canopy attached to radiating folding frame sliding on stick."
3. "Hinged or sliding barrier for closing entrance to building."
4. "Black lead enclosed in cylinder of wood with tapering end."
5. "Pronged instrument used for eating at table."
6. "Backless seat for one."
7. "Man's sleeved, usually cloth, body garment."

(Answers start on page 183.)

19

ROLLING ALONG

If you and your friends find a nice soft grassy hill when you're out for a walk, why not try rolling down it.

Lie down in a straight line, arms by your sides, and, at a given signal, start rolling. Anyone who so much as touches someone else must go back and start again.

PASS THE MATCHBOX

Divide the players into two teams, then push the cover from an empty matchbox onto the nose of the first player in each team. At the word "Go," the players must pass the matchbox covers along the line, from one nose to the next, without touching it with their hands.

21

PLATE SPINNING

The best plates to use for this game are plastic or enamel. You need just one plate and a flat surface to spin it on.

The players sit in a circle and each one has a number which is written on a card, and then placed in a hat. One player stands with the plate in the middle of the circle and another player stands outside the circle with the hat full of numbered cards. The plate is set spinning and the spinner steps quickly to one side as the player with the hat picks and calls out a number. The player with that number has to leap up and catch the plate before it stops spinning. Don't be fooled—this is not as easy as it sounds.

22

BOTTLE CAP BATTLE

Arrange twelve bottle caps in a circle with their edges touching. Now take turns with a friend to remove either one or two bottle caps. If you choose to take two, they must be touching each other.

The person who takes the last bottle cap or touching pair is the winner.

STAMP COLLECTOR

Ideal as a party game, Stamp Collector needs a little preparation before the guests arrive.

    You need an inexpensive packet of unused foreign stamps, unused because you will be making use of their not-too-sticky glue. Stick them all over the room or even all over the house, in unusual and difficult places. Give your guests some clues as to where the stamps are hidden and as to what they are looking for, such as "A member of the British royal family is in the kitchen tonight," or "An Italian greyhound is waiting near the front door."

24

PEN NAMES

Many famous authors have used pen names. Do you know who these people were in real life?
1. Currer Bell
2. Mark Twain
3. George Orwell
4. George Eliot
5. Saki
6. Lewis Carroll

(Answers start on page 183.)

PUSH OF WAR

This is exactly what it sounds like: the exact opposite of a Tug Of War.

Mark out three parallel lines on the ground, each about 10 feet (3 m) apart. Lay a rope along the middle line. Two teams of eight or ten people each must line up, side by side, facing each other across the rope. At a given signal they pick up the rope and try to push it over the line behind the opposing team.

26

MIND READING

Tell your audience you can read minds with no trouble at all. Ask a volunteer to choose any number between 1 and 9, but not to say it out loud. Then give the following list of instructions:

Multiply by 3.

Add 1.

Multiply by 3.

Add the number first thought of.

Tell you the number he now has.

It will be a two-digit number ending in 3. Remove the 3 and you will be left with the number he first thought of. You have read his mind!

RICE TRAILING

On a fine day play hare and hounds with a trail of rice or corn. The hare sets off ten minutes ahead of everyone else, carrying a big bag of rice or corn, and scatters a handful here and there. If two paths diverge, he leaves a handful in the middle of the path he has taken.

The hounds then set off to follow the trail. Do not leave later than ten minutes after the hare, in case the birds eat up all the rice or corn in the meanwhile!

28

TUNE TAPPING

This is a good game for a car trip, as it needs no equipment whatsoever. Just tap out the rhythm of a well known song with your finger on the cover of this book—or on the seat if it makes more noise—and see who can guess the tune first.

29

BURST THE BAG

Can you run a relay race and still have enough puff to blow up a paper bag? Try it.

Divide the players into two teams and send the first two off to run around the block. Hand each one a paper bag as they come back to the starting point.

The second member of each team is not allowed to set off until the bag has been successfully blown up and burst. If you can't get bags that burst properly, just blow them up to full capacity instead.

AUSTRALIAN STICK GAME

Divide the players into two teams and mark a base line. The first player from each team walks out from the line and places three sticks, like the rungs of a ladder, ahead of him. Both players must then return to the base line and run out, over the sticks without touching them, and, starting from the last stick, finish with a long jump. The player who covers the longer distance from his first stick to the end of his jump is the winner of that round.

After the first round, the winners from each team compete against each other, until you determine the one player with the largest jump of all.

31

CHEAT

Take a pack of cards and deal them all out among you. The object of the game is to get rid of all your cards as soon as possible. This is how you do it. The first player places some of his cards face down on the table. He then says what they are, though the cards themselves might be quite different. The next player must then place down some of his own cards and say they are either the same cards as the player before, or as the next card up or the next card down. Of course, he may be cheating as well.

At any time, any of the other players may challenge the cards that have been put on the table. If someone is caught cheating, he must pick up all the cards that are on the table and the play begins again. You may end up with a huge handful to get rid of.

No player can pass, so sometimes you are forced to cheat. So, when you have only a few cards left, you need to sound very convincing.

1

J-U-N-E

Ask all the players to sit in a circle. They then take turns shouting out a word, the first player giving a word beginning with J, the second with U, and third with N and fourth with E (Jam, Umbrella, Nuts, Egg, perhaps). Then they continue, with the fifth player shouting a different word beginning with J, the sixth with U, and so on. Any player who fails to think of a word beginning with the right letter is out of the game. Of course, no word can be used more than once.

2

TOTAL SURRENDER

For this game, players must split into two teams of equal numbers of players, and scatter to opposite ends of the playing field. At a given signal (a whistle from a non-player), the two teams approach each other warily. The aim is for each player to select an opponent and then try to pin him to the ground with both shoulders flat. The contest is strictly on a one-to-one basis. If two players select the same opponent, then both are out of the contest at once.

When all pairs have one player pinned down, the team with the most members on top wins.

HOG TIE

Select two players of equal height, size and weight. Then hand each one a 6-foot (2-m) length of rope. Position players about 10 yards (9 m) apart.

At a given signal, each player approaches the other warily, rope in hand. Each must try to tie the other up in a hog tie, with a square knot around the ankles, while trying to stop the other player from doing the same to him. If no one has had any success after five minutes, let two more contestants try their luck.

4

GOLDFISH!

For this summer party game you need two goldfish bowls, each about two-thirds full of water. One bowl must contain a live goldfish and the other bowl should contain about eight table tennis balls, all bobbing about on the surface. Now ask for volunteers.

Give the first player a peashooter, or a supply of drinking straws or a tube of any kind which he or she can use to suck in air. The player must, by suction only, try to pick up the table tennis balls on the end of his or her air tube and put them one by one on the table—and this must be done against the clock!

Whoever gets all the balls out in the shortest time is the winner. The winner's prize is, of course, the goldfish.

5

DART BOARDS

If you have or can borrow a set of darts, you could make some paper "targets" for some informal games with friends.

Cut out a circle of stiff paper about 18 inches (45 cm) in diameter and draw lines across the middle to divide the circle into eight segments. Draw a small circle in the middle for the bull's eye and draw a narrow margin around the edge. Write a number in each segment. Pin the paper "target" onto a cork noteboard or a piece of cardboard and mark a line for the players to stand, about 8 feet (2.5 m) away.

Each player has a turn throwing three darts. A hit in the bull's eye scores 20, the segments score as they are marked, and a hit in the margin scores double the number in that segment.

The first player to reach 100 is the winner.

6

SPOTTERS

This is a good game to play during a car trip. Before you set off, make a list of the animals you may be able to spot, and agree on a points system for them—

> 1 for a dog or cat
> 2 for a horse, cow, or sheep
> 3 for a bull or goat
> 4 for a deer or rabbit

and so on.

Now see who can score the most points during the journey. Score 6 for any animal seen which is not on the list.

X MARKS THE SPOT

Prepare two identical sketch maps of the scene of an imaginary crime and mark out the paper in 1-inch (25-mm) squares.

Divide the players into two teams and position them at the opposite end of the room from the maps. Each team has a large blank sheet of paper marked out in 3-inch (75-mm) squares and a couple of soft-tip pens.

Each team sends one player at a time to look at the map for 30 seconds. Then come back and draw as much of it as possible on the large sheet of paper. The next player then goes and fills in some more on his or her return.

Which team has made the better copy? Or have they both fallen into the trap and used the wrong scale? The new maps, with 3-inch (75-mm) squares, should be three times as big as the original map.

8

CHINESE BOXING

Try this form of boxing without any boxing gloves. Stand facing a partner, about a yard (meter) away, and grasp his or her left wrist with your right hand. You must each hold your other arm straight out at shoulder level. At the word "Go," try to tap each other with the outstretched hand, at the same time trying to push the other player's hand out of the way.

When one of you has scored five taps, change hands and try again.

9   **June**

WHAT AM I?

Try this riddle:
My first is in fish which is good to eat
My second in rat but not in beat!
My third is in oil but not in sail,
My fourth in gate and also in gale.
My whole is an animal small and green
Hiding near pools and seldom seen.

(Answers start on page 183.)

10

THE FERRYMAN

Mark two chalk lines on a playground or sidewalk, about 6 feet (2 m) apart, and pretend that the area between them is a fast-flowing river. You, as ferryman, have to get all your team across, but all you have is a small raft made out of a tin tray. (The tray has a hole in it at one end with a rope tied through it. The other end of the rope is tied around your waist.)

Challenge another team to a race, and start with one team member sitting on each tray, waiting for the word "Go!" You must now drag the first team member across the river, then, when he or she leaps off, you go back for the next, and so on.

The team that ferries all its players across the river first wins.

11

RHYMING STORY

Try telling a rhyming story just for fun. The first player makes up one line. The second player gives a line to rhyme with it, then adds another line. The third player does the same, and so on.

Here is an example to start you off:

1st person:	One day out on a hill we went.
2nd person:	And in a field we pitched our tent
	Because we really loved to camp
3rd person:	Unless the grass was very damp.
	We all hate fog and wind and rain
4th person:	But when the sun comes out again

. . . and so on.

12

MYSTERY TEN

Place ten sticks or drinking straws on a table to make a figure that looks like this:

$$XI + I = X$$

Of course that cannot be right, as 11 plus 1 makes 12 and not 10. The equation can easily be put right without moving a single number. How is it done? Think carefully. There are two solutions. Time limit: 2 minutes.

(Answers start on page 183.)

13

TABLE BALL

If you have a round picnic table with a hole for an umbrella in the middle, you have the ideal table for a game of table ball. If you don't have a table like this, drive a post into the ground alongside a square or rectangular table.

Tie an empty thread spool on a piece of string and fix this to the pole or umbrella as a swinging weight. Write numbers on an assortment of plastic bottles or tin cans and stand them on the table.

Then, swing the weight to knock down as many bottles as possible, and add up your score.

Now challenge a friend to a game.

14

T.V. STARS

With this simple game you can provide entertainment at a family party.

Divide the guests into two teams and ask each team to select a famous T.V. personality. One member of the team must then dress up like that personality, if possible, and give a little performance in that person's style, using appropriate catchphrases, gestures, and so on.

The other team then has one of its members portray the T.V. personality they chose.

Continue taking turns selecting and portraying different "stars" until all players have had a chance to demonstrate their acting abilities.

No one wins or loses in this game.

ANAGRAMS

This game needs a little preparation. Write a list of anagrams on pieces of paper and give a copy to each of your friends. The first person to unscramble all the words is the winner, or you can set a time limit so that the person who discovers the most words in a given time, wins.

It is a good idea to choose words of a similar kind, such as countries or the names of famous people.

16

HORSES AND RIDERS

Try this game with pairs of players of equal weight so that horses and jockeys can change places—or pair off so that heavier players are the horses and lightweight players are the jockeys. Play on soft grass or on a sandy beach so no one gets hurt.

The rules are simple: one jockey tries to pull another off his horse on a strictly one-to-one basis. The horse can help by moving in close or backing away, but is not allowed to push or use its hands.

When you have unseated one jockey, move on to another. The winner is the last one left in the saddle.

BLINDFOLD BALLGAME

Divide the players into two teams and put a large ball in the middle of a room where you have removed the furniture. Blindfold one player from each team and get him or her to crawl towards the ball—which someone has moved to another part of the room.

Each team may shout instructions to help its players reach the ball, but there is bound to be plenty of confusion before someone does.

18

WHICH LEAF?

Make a collection of as many different leaves as you can, and keep a note of where you found them. Press the leaves between the pages of an old book and put them away until the fall.

In the fall, collect a brightly colored version of each leaf and press these, too. Use a reference book to help you identify all the spring and fall collections, or get the advice of a botany teacher.

Arrange all the leaves on a corkboard for a quiz. Mix them all up to make it really difficult, or arrange them in their pairs to make guessing a little easier.

CAR CONTEST

If you have any friends who are really interested in cars, you can put their knowledge to the test. Cut pictures of parts of cars—wheels, headlights, bumpers, doors—out of advertisements, or take photos of car parts, and glue them onto cards. Write a number on the back of each card, and make a master list of what type of car each piece was cut from.

Get your friends to write down the make of car for each card. Then compare their answers with your master list.

20

SHAPES AND THINGS

Give everyone a plain postcard and a pencil and ask them to close their eyes and make six dots anywhere they like on the card. Collect the cards, shuffle them, and hand them out again. Each player must now draw an object using those six dots as the main points in the drawing. Prizes go to the funniest and most original efforts.

21

PASS THE ORANGE

You can either play this game in two teams or stand around together in one circle. The object is simply to pass an orange from one person to another, using only the chins and the shoulders. If you are using two teams, you can make it a race, but it is always very funny whichever way you play.

22

DON'T SAY IT

Get a group of friends together. Choose a word that people use a lot in conversation like "yes" or "no," but don't choose "and" or "I" because you'll find it makes the game too difficult.

Now, just carry on talking together, but try to avoid using the word you have chosen. If you say it, you lose a point. At the end of an agreed period of time, the person who has lost the least points is the winner.

HOLIDAYS

Summer is the time for vacations—and for holidays. Can you make 38 words of 3 or more letters each out of the word HOLIDAYS?

(Answers start on page 183.)

24

SLEEPING PIRATE

A similar version of this very old game of skill was played by children in Roman times. It is best to play on a warm, windless day.

One player, the Pirate, sits blindfolded on a log or stool with an empty matchbox at his or her feet. The other players form a wide circle around him, say 40 to 50 yards (36-45 m) away. They have to approach the Pirate stealthily and snatch the matchbox from his feet without his knowledge. The first to do so is the winner.

If the Pirate hears your breathing or movements, he claps his hands and points to you. If he's right, you're out of the game.

BROKEN EGG

If you like a messy game, this one is always a lot of fun, but remember to play it outdoors!

Divide up into pairs, facing each other in two lines. One person of each pair has an egg. At the word "Go," the player with the egg throws it gently to his partner, and then takes a step backwards. His partner then throws the egg back, and takes a step back himself. Carry on throwing the egg and stepping backwards until you reach a line drawn along the ground 15 feet (4.5 m) behind your original starting position. The first pair to cross the finishing lines successfully wins. By then they will be 30 feet (9 m) apart. Long before then most of the eggs will be broken in somebody's hands! (If you don't want to waste eggs, just use a ball instead.)

26

COLORFUL THOUGHTS

In this game, one player thinks of an object and then says what color it is, for example: "I am thinking of something red." Other players can then take turns asking questions to which the first one may answer only "Yes" or "No." Every time a player gets the answer "Yes," he is allowed to guess what the object is, and when someone guesses correctly, he or she then takes over the "thinking" role.

STRING ALONG

Divide your friends into two equal teams and give each team a long piece of string. At the word "Go," the first member of each team passes the string down through his clothing and gives the end to the next in line. The next person does exactly the same until all the members of the team are all strung together. The first team to finish the line wins.

28

EUROPEAN TOUR

Imagine that you are going to go on a tour of Europe this summer. In which cities would you expect to find these famous sights?

1. St. Peter's Basilica
2. Eiffel Tower
3. Big Ben
4. Bridge of Sighs
5. Louvre
6. Spanish Riding School
7. Prado
8. Tivoli Gardens

(Answers start on page 183.)

29

WET
DAY
RACE

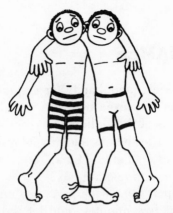

Choose a day when it is really wet out and there is a good deal of mud about and try a three-legged race. Change into swimming gear first, then team up with a partner and tie your inside legs together firmly with a handkerchief. Try a few practice runs on your own, then challenge other pairs to a race across the muddiest course you can find.

30

NIAGARA

On June 30, 1859, Charles Blondin (real name Jean Francois Gravelet) walked across Niagara Falls on a tightrope.

Try walking along a broom handle laid flat on the floor, and you will be able to imagine how he felt. Ask two friends to sit on top of the ends of the handle to stop it from rolling, and carry a long cane or beanpole to add to the effect and help you to balance.

Now can you do it backwards?

INSTANT NAMES

Keep this "quickie" game handy for a spare five minutes at your party. It can be played by teams or individuals.

Write the letters of the alphabet on pieces of paper and put them in a box. Write themes such as "Boys' names," "Girls' names," "Animals," "Pets," "Cars," etc., on more pieces of paper and put them in another box.

Draw one paper from each box, set an alarm clock or kitchen timer for five minutes, and let the players see how many names they can write down in the time limit, each beginning with the letter of the alphabet that is marked on the first piece of paper, and keeping strictly to the theme that is marked on the other paper.

The player who thinks of the most names is the winner.

2

SIMON SAYS

Ask for a volunteer to be Simon. All he has to do is to stand in the middle of the room and shout instructions. "Simon says stand up. Simple Simon says arms in the air. Simon says touch the wall," and so on.

Now and again he must forget the "Simon says" and just shout an instruction, like "Sit down."

Anyone who begins to do anything that Simple Simon didn't tell him to do is out.

3

FOLLOW ON

This is a word game to play in a group. First, you choose the type of words that you want to use, like countries or names of towns or famous people, or perhaps try verbs only.

Now, one person starts and says a word in the category that has been chosen. The next person has three seconds to say another word in the same category which begins with the last letter of the previous word. The game continues around the circle of people and anyone who cannot think of a word in time, has to drop out. The winner is the last one left.

If you have chosen cities, the sequence might go like this: New York, Kiev, Vienna, Adelaide, Edinburgh, Hyderabad, Dijon, and so on.

4

INDEPENDENCE DAY QUIZ

Today is, of course, Independence Day. But do you know your history?

1. In what year was American independence declared?
2. Who was the second President of the United States?
3. In which city was the Declaration of Independence issued?
4. Only one U.S. President has come from Kentucky. Which one?

(Answers start on page 183.)

BOWLORAMA

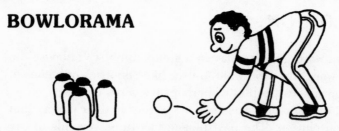

You can make a set of bowling pins very easily from a set of plastic bottles (complete with lids). If they are all the same size and shape, so much the better.

Put a little earth or sand into each bottle to make it heavier, but not too heavy, and lay them out in the usual way—four in the back row, three in the next, then two, and one in front. Roll a rubber ball or tennis ball at them from about 20 feet (6 m) back.

Be prepared to experiment a little. If the pins knock over much too easily, add more sand or earth; but if they are too difficult to shift, take a little out.

6

ANIMAL PORTRAITS

Play this game out-of-doors, perhaps on a picnic. Each player collects a pile of stones, leaves, twigs, etc., and then arranges them on a sheet of newspaper to make an animal portrait.

Let all players act as judges, each giving three points for the best portrait, two for the second, and one for the third—and none for his own!

Then, everyone arranges a second portrait, and everyone judges these. The player with the combined highest score is the winner.

THE COLLECTIVE GAME

Many birds are given special collective names when they flock together. Do you know the names of the birds which complete the following phrases?

1. A wisp of
2. A parliament of
3. A nye of
4. An exaltation of
5. A covey of
6. A skein (or gaggle) of
7. A charm of
8. A bevy of
9. A spring of
10. A murmuration of

(Answers start on page 183.)

8

THE STRING GAME

One thing
To which I cling
like anything
is String . . .
But when I unwind it
I wish I could find it!

Ask your family and friends to collect for you any odd pieces of string or cord and a few bottles with interesting shapes. Now all you need is some glue and some nimble-fingered friends. Have a contest to see who can decorate a bottle the neatest and in the shortest time by winding string around and around to cover it completely.

Successful results can be painted, filled with sand or pebbles, and used as lamp bases.

DUCKS AND DRAKES

Search around on beaches and lakesides and the banks of
slow-flowing rivers for round, thin, flat stones. Try skipping
them over the water so that they jump across the surface. (The
secret is to hold and throw them parallel with the water's
surface and to give a good flick with the wrist.) Two or three
jumps are good, and six or seven are excellent.

10

TEAM CHARIOTS

This game comes from Pennsylvania, where it is a popular
camp game in summer. Three heavy sticks are tied together to
form a neat triangle which is the chariot. Each chariot has a
team of two "horses" and one "driver." The horses face the
same way and lift the trestle triangle up, one with the right
hand, the other with the left; the outside hands are free. The
driver, a lightweight, now stands on either stick behind them,
near the ground. He has both hands on the front stick.

That is the starting position of each chariot. The race can
be around a circuit or down a straight stretch, but should take
place on sand or grass in case anyone falls. It's amazing how
fast the chariots can go, and how skillful the drivers can
become at manipulating the horses.

LONGEST WORDS

Have a contest to see who can write down the longest words containing this list of two-letter combinations.

For example, the first two combinations are OM and MB, and the words could be cOMpetition and coMBination. Set a five-minute time limit, and then compare answers.

OM	UC	ES
MB	EL	RT
OS	NC	OU
		VE

12

ANKLE GRABBERS

Every time you play this game you get better at it. You and your opponent must kneel and face each other and try and grab each other's ankles. You are not allowed to get off your knees, but you can lie down if you wish. Whatever you do, your knees must still be on the ground. When either of you grasps the other's ankles firmly, as opposed to merely touching them, you are the winner, and can go on to challenge someone else.

FOOTPRINTS

This is a really messy outdoor game, but it's a lot of fun. Every player has to mark his or her footprints on a sheet of stiff white paper. Mix up lots of poster paint and pour plenty of it onto big sheets of plywood. Step barefoot in this glorious mess and out onto a sheet of white paper. Write your name on the back of the paper and leave it to dry while you hurry straight to a pail of clean warm water to get the poster paint off your feet. Later, you can see if you can recognize everyone's footprints.

14

INDOOR FRENCHIE

Today is Bastille Day in France. In honor of July 14, play this French ball game.

Frenchie is the nickname for French cricket. Try the indoor version using a table tennis paddle and ball.

The game is best played in a hall or large room from which most of the furniture has been removed. The first batsman stands in the middle of the room, and holds the paddle in one hand. He must keep his knees and feet tightly together, but can turn around if he wishes.

The other players form a circle around him and throw the ball so as to try to hit him below the knee. Surprise, speed, and a spin with the fingers are the secrets of attack.

When the batsman is hit he hands over the paddle to the person who "bowled" him, and that player becomes the new batsman.

NUMBERS, NUMBERS

Careful preparation is needed for this game. Have a look around to see how many pocket calculators you can borrow. Now write down some lengthy calculations and work them out. Something like this is ideal: $59 - 17 + 23 \div 5 \times 25 + 19 + 182 - 74 \div 2 \times 12 = 2712$.

When you are about to play the game, divide the players into as many teams as there are calculators and put the calculators at the other end of the room. Read out one of the calculations (minus its answer, of course). The teams then rush to a calculator and work it out. Whichever team comes up with the correct answer first is the winner.

16
BLOW IT

Divide the players into two teams. Now ask the members of one team to take deep breaths and puff out their cheeks to the fullest extent, and stay like that as long as possible. Members of the other team may do whatever they like to make them let the air out—anything, that is, except touch them. The champion is the last to "blow it." Now let the other team have a go at it. Finally, play the two champions off against each other.

(If you start feeling dizzy, be sure to "blow it!")

SPONGY

Play this game on a hot day when no one will mind getting wet!

Divide the players into two teams and give each team a sponge, a cup, and an empty bucket. Place two full buckets of water about 20 yards (18 m) away.

At the word "Go," the first player from each team runs to the bucket of water and fills his cup, *using only the sponge*. He then runs back, empties the cup into his team's empty bucket, and hands the sponge and cup to the next player in his team.

When all players have run the race, measure the water in the buckets to decide which team has won by filling up its pail the most.

18

MAGIC CARPET

All you need for this game is an old mat or carpet, about 3 feet (1 m) long and 1 foot (25 mm) wide. Two people can play at a time. One stands on the Magic Carpet and the other does his best to get him off it. No football tackles are allowed, but gentle wrestling is OK once pulling and tugging have failed.

MEMORY CIRCLES

Play this game in a large hall where you are allowed to chalk on the floor. Divide the players into four groups and draw a circle on the floor for each group. Now stand by the light switch. The players must walk around and around the room and to and fro across it. Then, when the lights go out, they must go as quickly as possible to stand in their circle.

Switch the lights back on and see just how many have made it back to their own circle!

20

ABC QUIZ

This is a memory game for any number of players, each of whom needs a pencil and paper.

Ask a volunteer to write a list of ten words beginning with A, ten beginning with B, and ten beginning with C. He must now read the list out loud twice, very slowly. The other players have five minutes to remember and write down all the words they can remember. The player who remembers the most words correctly gets 3 points.

Now try again with a second volunteer taking the letters D, E and F, and so on. Leave out letters Q, X and Z unless you want the game to last all night!

When you have worked your way through the alphabet, total up the winning scores from each set and see who the winner is.

GRAB!

Lie face downwards on soft grass, side by side with your opponent, and both of you do a push-up, supported on straight arms, hands and toes on the ground, and bodies in a straight line. Now you must each try to upset your opponent by grabbing his wrist quickly and making him collapse to the ground while you recover your push-up to win the contest.

22

THE AMBUSH

You will have to wait for a dark, moonless, dry, mild night to play this game. The idea is for small groups of Attackers to run the gauntlet through the game area without being ambushed by the Defenders. This can only be done by stealth: Attackers must crawl on all-fours, control their breathing, avoid dry twigs that snap loudly, hide behind trees, and use shrubs and plants as cover.

The Defenders should plan their ambush routine beforehand, perhaps allowing a group which has been spotted to progress until they run into a neat ambush from both sides.

Make up more rules of your own to suit your territory and the numbers playing.

ANIMALS AND THEIR MATES

A female lion is a lioness. Can you guess the names of the females for the following species?

1. Dog
2. Billy goat
3. Fox
4. Stallion
5. Stag
6. Cob (swan)
7. Ram
8. Peacock

(Answers start on page 183.)

24

THE SNAKE GAME

In this game for any number of players, each person is given a double sheet of newspaper and asked to turn it into a snake. It is not a race against the clock but a competition to see who can make the longest snake simply by tearing the paper.

The snake must be one continuous strip of paper without any breaks at all, but it can be as thin and wriggly as you like.

25

CLATTERING CANS

Gather together 25 used soft drink cans and stack them up in a pyramid—a line of 9 cans for the base, 7 on top, 5 on top of them, then 3, then 1 on the very top. Stand well back and see how many you or your friends can knock over by throwing a tennis ball at them.

Now try it with a rolled-up pair of socks instead of a ball. It will be much more difficult.

TUG OF WAR

This is best played with two teams of 6-8 people each. Use a rope one inch (25 mm) in diameter and tie a handkerchief on it to mark the middle point. Make three marks in a straight line on the ground, 6 feet (2 m) apart, and lay the rope along them, the handkerchief on the middle mark.

The teams can now pick up the rope and, at a given signal, start pulling. When one team has pulled the other over the 6-foot (2-m) mark and the handkerchief crosses the mark at their end, that team has won.

The best of three or five pulls decides the overall winner.

27

TEN TON FINGERS

Lay your hand flat on the table with all the fingers straight out. Now bend the middle finger under. Tell yourself your thumb weighs ten tons. Can you lift it? Your little finger weighs as much as an elephant. Can you lift it without moving any of the other fingers? Your forefinger weighs as much as a car. Can you lift it? Your ring finger is as light as a feather. But can you lift it? Well, can you? Have a go yourself, then try this trick on a friend.

GUESS THEIR AGES

a) Robert is twice as old as Peter used to be when Robert was as old as Peter is now. Peter is now 18. How old is Robert?

b) Jane is twice as old as Elizabeth was when Jane was her age. When Elizabeth is as old as Jane is now, the sum of their ages will be 99. How old are they both?

c) John's grandfather is 87½ years old. His grandmother is only 50. How many years ago was his grandfather 2¼ times as old as his grandmother?

(Answers start on page 183.)

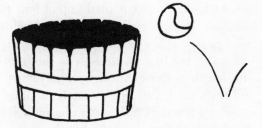

29

TUB BALL

The best kind of tub for this game is a wooden one used for patio plants and shrubs, or one made from sawing a small barrel in half. In addition, you need a good supply of tennis balls.

Each player stands about 10 or 15 feet (3-5 m) back from the tub and has three tries at throwing a ball into the tub so that it stays there. An easier way is to bounce the ball in—one bounce on the ground and then into the tub.

The player who succeeded in getting the most balls to land in the tub is the winner. If there is a tie among players, these players continue competing with each other until there is only one winner.

BEACH BALL RACES

You can devise all kinds of unusual races using large beach balls, one for each player. Try:

      kicking the ball backwards;
      running with the ball between the knees;
      waddling with the ball between the ankles;
      kneeling, pushing the ball with the forehead;
      hopping, kicking the ball with one leg.

31

BEN HUR

This chariot race is best run in bare feet on a sandy, firm beach. Each chariot is made up of four people. Two of them are linked together with arms folded behind their backs. The third person is the pivot who packs down behind them, football style, holding on strongly to the front pair by their arms. The fourth is the charioteer, who jumps on the pivot's back and rests his hands one on each shoulder of the front pair.

After a few trial runs, your chariot will be able to challenge another to a race along the beach.

PANDEMONIUM

This is just as much fun to watch as it is to play, and it is ideal for parties.

Six volunteers pick a folded sheet of instructions out of a hat. Three will find that their note reads: "When a newspaper is placed on the floor, you must do all in your power to keep it neatly folded on the floor." The other three will open notes reading: "When a newspaper is placed on the floor, you must tear it apart and throw the pieces high in the air."

The biggest Sunday paper ever suddenly appears on the floor as if by magic, and pandemonium breaks loose!

2

BALL-IN-THE-BOX

After a game like Pandemonium there is bound to be a lot of litter about, so why not use it for another game? Collect all the bits of paper and roll them into two big tight balls wrapped very firmly around with Scotch tape. Now, divide the players into two teams and ask them to stand in line. Each team has a goalie who stands at the end of the line holding a cardboard box.

Starting at the other end, the ball is passed from player to player, using only the palm of the hand. If the ball drops to the ground, then it must start again at the back of the line. The winning team is the first to get the ball in the box.

THE BADGER

Make a "badger" from a paper bag filled with rustling paper,
a can filled with small stones, or a can with keys tied on it.
Tie a rope to the "badger" and blindfold the players. Now tug
the badger across the floor so that it makes a noise, and see if
anyone can grab it. Of course the badger can keep quiet
whenever it suits him.

Swap the "badger" rope for the blindfold of anyone who
catches it.

4

INDIAN PISTOL

This game is based on Sleeping Indian (November 21) and is
best played on a beach on a hot day. The Sleeping Indian has
a bunch of keys at his feet, which the stalker is going to try
to pick up and take back to base. But the Indian also has a
water pistol and a bucket of water for re-filling it. When the
Indian thinks he hears a sound, he fires a shot of water in the
direction of the noise instead of pointing a finger. You will
find he rarely hits the right target and anyone can be in the
firing line!

CAPTURE THE CASTLE

This can be a very boisterous game, and is best played with two teams of five or six people each. One team must link arms in a solid circle to make the Castle. Somewhere outside the Castle, plotting its downfall and capture, are the Attackers. Their aim is to get inside the Castle, and capture it. Violence is taboo, but they may crawl between legs or under and over arms.

Each team takes a turn as Castle and Attackers, and the "attack" is timed. The team that makes the quickest capture wins.

6

CORKO

Collect as many bottle corks as you can, give six to each player, and ask them to write their names on them in ballpoint or felt pen. All the players should form a large circle around a plastic bucket and try to flick each of their corks into it. (To flick a cork, put it on the flat palm of one hand and flick with the thumb and forefinger of the other.) Who gets the most corks into the bucket out of his or her six?

ACTION PAINTING

Fill a small plastic bag with poster paint, tie the top, and hang it from a low tree branch. Spread out a large sheet of paper underneath the branch and then snip off a tiny corner of the bag. Set the bag swinging and stand clear while your action painting paints itself.

8

YOUR MOVE NEXT

Mark out a big square or rectangle on the sidewalk in chalk (or draw it on paper indoors). Sub-divide it into about six or eight compartments of about the same size and number them. Then place one *large* single item in each small square—an item of clothing, a stool, a basketball, anything like that. Let the players try to memorize the objects, then send them away for a minute. Rearrange the items so that almost all of them are in different squares.

Call the players back and ask them to say which items have been moved. At first this should not be too difficult. Then try the game again with two or three small items in each square and move them about in varying combinations. This is much more of a challenge.

9

NAME THE GIRL

Have you ever noticed how many girls' names end in the letter A? See if you can make a list of one "A" name for every letter of the alphabet. Here are three to start you off: Agatha, Belinda, Cora.

ONE LETTER AT A TIME

Here's another brain teaser! To solve each question, just change one letter in the previous answer. You start with the word TIME.

1. Definitely not wild.
2. Exactly similar.
3. Bargain buy time in a department store.
4. A boy is one and so is a man.
5. Story.
6. Bind.
7. Stare at.
8. American football is a man's one!
9. Win an Olympic gold medal and you're certain of this.
10. Destiny.
11. April 1, 1980.
12. Small freshwater fish.
13. You need them to play Monopoly and board games.
14. Mickey and Minnie Mouse.

(Answers start on page 183.)

11

SAND CARTOONS

There's nothing like a hard stretch of firm clear sand after the tide has gone out—it makes an ideal drawing surface.

Try drawing a cartoon figure with a stick, but leave the head off. Now ask a friend to finish it for you and see if you have both been drawing the same character. Is it recognizable? If not, have another go at it. The tide will soon wash away any disasters.

MATCH BOX

Two players face each other with left hands behind their backs and right hands stretched out straight in front of them, the palms pointing downwards. An empty matchbox is placed on the back of each hand (not on the knuckles or fingers). Now each player must try to knock his or her opponent's matchbox off with any quick move or feint, while still retaining his or her own box on the back of the hand.

13

HOPPING RELAY

Divide the players into two teams and explain the rules. The first player in each team must hop across the room, around a chair, and back again before the second player in that team sets off. Players must keep their arms folded and hop on the same leg.

If this is too easy, find small obstacles to be hop-jumped over along the route.

The team that finishes first wins.

WILDLIFE SILHOUETTES

Have fun on a rainy afternoon by making wild animal or bird silhouettes to use later in a guessing game.

Trace the outlines of animals and birds from books and magazines and transfer them to colored paper. Cut them out, and glue them all onto a contrasting background. Yellow silhouettes look good on a black background, brown on green, or black bird shapes on pale blue.

Bring out your silhouettes when friends come to call and see how good their knowledge of wildlife is.

15

PROVERBIAL PROBLEM

This looks easy—very easy. But see if you can get the right answer in two minutes. All you have to do is find out which letter occurs most frequently in these proverbs—A or O—and then say by what number that letter occurs more than the other. You may write down nothing except the final answer. Take all five proverbs together.

All that glitters is not gold.
A bird in the hand is worth two in the bush.
A fool and his money are soon parted.
Only the brave deserve the fair.
Once bitten, twice shy.

(Answers start on page 183.)

FLY AROUND THE WORLD

You are allowed to take a plane to anywhere you like in the world—as long as you do so in alphabetical order. One player starts by saying "I am flying to . . ." and then adds the name of a city beginning with A—Amsterdam, perhaps. The next says, "I am flying to Barcelona"—or Bogotá, Birmingham, or anywhere else beginning with B. Take turns, working through the alphabet and, when you get to Z, start again at A, but name different places this time around. Any player who misses a turn is out.

17

BLIND TUG

Try this game when it has rained and the ground is really muddy and slippery underfoot. It is played exactly like Tug of War (July 26), with certain important variations.

First, all players must be blindfolded, and so they will rely on cheers of encouragement from their audience to know how well they are doing. Second, they should all wear swimming gear or old clothes. Now proceed as before.

If you know of a very shallow stream nearby, use it as the middle line. The team which succeeds in pulling an opponent into the water is the winner.

BUTTERFLIES AND MOTHS

Many butterflies and moths have names as strange and beautiful as themselves. Can you complete these eight names?

1. Tiger — tail
2. Great —fritillary
3. Mourning —
4. Grotes' under —
5. Questrin —
6. Pearly —
7. Weidemeyer's —
8. — sulphur

(Answers start on page 183.)

19

SHIPWRECKED

This is a good thinking game, best played in two teams, each with a paper and pencil. Imagine you have all been sailing on an old-time schooner in the Pacific and you have been badly hit by an unexpected storm. Shipwrecked with no radio, radar or any modern aids, your only hope is to pull away in the ship's dinghies for the attractive shores of a nearby deserted island. It has plenty of trees, water, some wildlife, wild fruits and rootcrops, and lots of shelter.

Each team of five can take 20 things with them in a boat, and must avoid overcrowding. What are the things that each team would take, and why? Allow plenty of time for team discussion, and then get together to compare lists.

SAY IT!

Tell one of your friends to wait outside the room while the rest of you decide on a word. Choose something unusual or funny, otherwise the game won't be as fun. When your friend comes back into the room, you are going to try and make him say the word you have chosen. So, when you are ready, call him back and begin to ask him questions or talk amongst yourselves and get him to join in. Gradually, you have to lead the conversation around so that he will say the key word. You'll all be laughing as he gets close.

21

CATCH THE BALLOON

Can you catch a balloon? Yes, of course. But can you catch it between your knees?

Let everyone have a try, five attempted catches each. The person throwing the balloon should stand about 5 feet (150 cm) away.

WORD-MAKING

Cut up 62 squares of cardboard, all the same size, and write a letter of the alphabet on each one. Write each of the vowels—a,e,i,o,u—on four cards each, and use two cards for each consonant. Now shuffle the cards and deal ten to each player.

Players now have five minutes to write down as many words as they can make from those ten letters. Use as many of the ten letters as you like to make a word, and use the letters more than once, but you cannot repeat any of the words you make.

Score one point per letter for each word you make. The winner is the player with the most points after three rounds.

23

SHADOWS
ON THE WALL

This is a photo quiz which has to be prepared on a sunny day well in advance.

Take 20 or 30 ordinary everyday things from the home (with your parents' permission), and photograph them in black-and-white, not directly, but as shadows cast on a white sheet or wall. You will need someone to help you to fix or hold the objects against the sun.

The shadow pictures will be most unusual and not very easy to identify. When you hold the quiz, set a time limit of 15 minutes for 20 objects.

WHO'S TICKLISH?

Play this game on the beach with one person acting as detective. Everyone else helps dig an enormous hole in the sand and sits in it, close together, feet and legs intertwined and jumbled up as much as possible. The legs are then all covered over with sand, leaving only the feet sticking out.

The detective has to find who each foot belongs to. The other players may shriek when other people's toes are touched, if they wish—and keep quiet when their own are tickled—if they can! This will make the detective's job that much harder.

25

DOGGO

Ask a friend to help you prepare this game in advance. You will need several unbreakable plates or saucers—disposable ones are best. Now choose some different items to be identified by smell. One item could be a slice of onion. Others could be a little grated nutmeg, some chopped mint, other herbs from the garden, concentrated fruit jelly, a small piece of orange, a few rose petals, a little ground coffee, some flavoring essences from the kitchen. . . .

Do not use more than a little of any one substance, or a strong-smelling one may overwhelm more delicate scents. Now blindfold your friends and bring them into the room one by one to test their powers of smell as you pass each plate in front of them.

LOBSTER POT

Two players sit on the floor back to back and bolt upright, their arms interlocked at the elbows. Now they must try to stand up without releasing their hold on each other's arms.

27

SCAVENGER HUNT

As this game takes you out and about in the neighborhood, why not keep the neighbors entertained and play it in odd or fancy dress.

    Play it in teams of twos or threes. Give each team a list of things it has to collect or find out, such as:

> a daisy
> a 1949 coin
> a popsicle stick
> the name of a movie showing locally
> a travel brochure
> a foreign stamp
> the telephone number of the nearest hospital
> the price of a hamburger

The winning team is the first to complete its list.

QUIZ FOR TRAVELERS

Summer is the time for vacations abroad. Just how much do you know about foreign countries?

1. Of which countries are these cities the capital?
   a. Oslo
   b. Vienna
   c. Lima

2. Where would you go to spend:
   a. yen
   b. dinars
   c. escudos

3. Where would you be likely to eat:
   a. zabaglione
   b. sauerkraut
   c. moussaka

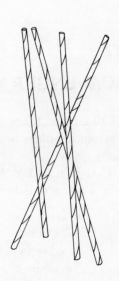

4. Where would you find:
   a. the Red Sea
   b. the Yellow River
   c. the Black Forest

(Answers start on page 183.)

29

THE MISSING SIX

For this game you need seven drinking straws. Can you lay them on the table in such a way that if you take one away you have none left?

(Answers start on page 183.)

BACKWARD SPELLING

Get a group of friends together and take turns being the leader. The leader calls out a word to each of the players in turn, choosing words of about the same degree of difficulty. As each player hears his word, he has ten seconds to spell it out loud—backwards! If he does it correctly, within the time limit, he scores a point.

After everybody has been leader a certain number of times, total the scores. The person with the highest score is the winner.

31

THE LEGPULL

This energetic game is played in pairs and needs the help of an umpire with a whistle. Play on soft grass in case anyone falls.

Stand facing your partner and clasp your right hands. Now you must each raise your right leg and grasp your opponent's right ankle with your left hand. Lean backwards to take the strain and begin to hop around in a clockwise direction.

The players must now react swiftly to three whistle signals. "*Pip*" means "reverse the direction of the hop." "*Pip pip*" means "hop and pull." "*Pip pip pip*" means "hop and push with stiff arms."

Try it and you'll want to keep going all night.

ANIMAL RACES

Hold a race over 100 yards (90 m) in which all competitors must imitate the same animal. Here are some suggestions to choose from:

> horses: on all fours
> crabs: on all fours, sideways
> monkeys: on all fours with legs straight
> penguins: with arms stiffly at the sides and feet
>> turned out
> kangaroos: jumping, feet together and arms folded.

2

HOP, STEP AND JUMP

Mark a well-defined base line on the ground, and off you go. Run up to the line, hop from the line on the right foot, landing on the right foot. Then take a big step off the right onto the left foot. Then jump off the left, landing with both feet together. Measure from the final landing place back to the base line.

See who can jump the longest distance and remember the record distance for the next time you play.

FRIEND OR FOE?

This is a game for bus or train journeys. Before you set off, make a list of things you are going to try to spot. Each one must have a descriptive color. For example, you might specify a red-and-white cow, a black-and-white cow, a black sheep, a black-faced sheep, a white dog, a pinto pony, a green house, a yellow car, a lady in a purple dress. The first player to spot any of these things shouts loudly *"Friend!"* He or she gains a point if correct. If not, everybody shouts at the top of their voices, *"No! Foe!"* The player who collects the most "friends" is the winner.

4

THE RAILROAD TUNNEL

Ask everybody to sit down in a circle on the floor and shut their eyes. You are all long-distance trains. Ask a volunteer to give a brief description of the freight you are carrying, the railroad you are on, and your destination. You are about to enter the longest tunnel on your route and the train will have to whistle.

Open your eyes and let everyone practice making a piercing whistle. Now appoint one player who will point to one person at a time without warning. He or she is the whistle of the train. The winner is the person who can whistle longest and loudest.

RING THE BOTTLE

Collect nine empty bottles—all identical if you can—and glue a paper number on each one. Now draw five rings on cardboard, each 4 inches (100 mm) in diameter and about ½ inch (15 mm) thick, and cut them out. (Check that they will fit over the bottles.)

Set up the bottles on the floor in three rows of three and see who can total up the highest score by throwing the rings over the bottles from a distance of about 5 feet (1.5 m). Sand in the bottles will help stop them from falling over if you hit them with the rings.

6

SORT OUT
THE NEWS

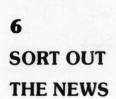

This is an ideal game for a party and the smaller the space it is played in, the better.

Each person is given a specially prepared newspaper which has all the pages in the wrong order, some of them upside down, one missing, and one extra (from one of the other newspapers).

The winner is the first person to sort out his newspaper and make it look neat and tidy, with all the pages together and in the right order.

FRUIT NAMES

Use this as a quick game to fill in an odd moment at a party. Who can think of seven different fruits, all of which can be people's surnames? Here are some examples, all of them real people:

Frank B. Apple, Christine Pear, Rupert Cherry, Albert Medlar, Peter Quince, Miss Lemon, Jack Orange.

Other spellings, such as Appel, Peare and Lemmon are also acceptable.

8

FLOORBALL

Use a basketball court to play this game. You need two teams of five players each and a referee. Play for seven minutes each way with a short break at half-time.

The two teams line up on either side of the half-way mark on the basketball court and the referee throws the ball up to start. Players can catch and throw the ball to other members of their team or run along bouncing the ball with one hand. They can't run holding the ball. There is no offside so players can move forwards freely and pass aside or ahead.

At either end of the court a goal is marked on the floor, about 5 feet (1.5 m) wide. Each team has a goalie who can defend the goal with both hands and his legs, but he can't kick the ball. To score a goal, shoot the ball with a swift push of the hand. At the end of the game, the team with the most goals wins. The referee must decide during play if anyone is breaking the rules.

HAZARDS

Mark out a playing area about 6 feet (2 m) wide and 12 feet
(3.5 m) long, with a wall at the far end. Find 12 large stones
and dot them about over the area. Now take turns rolling a
tennis ball from the base line so that it hits the wall, touching
as few stones as possible on the way. Remember that the ball
must be kept on the ground at all times.

A point is scored each time the ball touches a stone. The
winner is the player with the lowest score after rolling the ball
ten times.

10

NAME THAT MAN!

If you are with several people who all know each other—
family, friends or classmates—you could try this game just
for fun.

Send one player out of the room and blindfold him. While
he is out, ask for a volunteer to read a few lines from a book.
On his return, the blindfolded player must guess who is reading.

It is amazing how many people have the same voice pat-
terns and how many mistakes will be made.

HIGH DICE,
LOW DICE

Search around for as many dice as you can find. Now divide
into two teams so that every member of each team has his own
dice.

All the players throw their dice at the same time. Each
team adds up the total of all its dice. In High Dice, the
winning team is the one with the highest score; in Low Dice
it's the opposite. Alternatively, you could aim to be the
closest to a predetermined score of 24 or so. Keep a running
total to determine the final winning team after a certain
number of rounds.

If you don't have that many dice, the members of each team
can take it in turns to throw, but the game is much more
exciting if everyone is throwing dice at once.

12

MANHATTAN GOLF

For this game you need nine large sheets of drawing or wrapping paper numbered 1−9 and a plastic plate per player. Lay
the sheets of paper on the ground over a large "course"—say
50 yards (45 m) between each paper—and weight them down
with small stones.

Each sheet of paper represents a "hole" and players must
skim their plates to land on them. Each hole may take two or
three shots or more. Count up the score—the lowest wins.

ZODIAC QUIZ

How well do you know the signs of the Zodiac? Can you remember all of them, and do you know what they mean?

1. How many signs of the Zodiac are there?
2. Which sign is linked with weighing and balancing?
3. Which sign is named after the King of Beasts?
4. Which signs sound rather wet?
5. Which sign would you not allow in a china shop?
6. How many signs are named after animals of one kind or another?

(Answers start on page 183.)

14

NATURE QUIZ

Play this as a team game unless you know the players are wildlife enthusiasts and could work alone.

Collect pictures of native wild birds from magazines, write a number on each one, and paste them onto a large sheet of paper that can be pinned on the wall. (Black and white photographs will make the birds harder to identify than colored ones.)

Give all the players a pencil and paper—and a time limit to name as many birds as they can. Keep a separate list of the answers.

An easier version of this game would be to use pictures of wild animals native to the United States.

MATH GENIUS?

Challenge two friends to see who can add the fastest. You can bet your life it will be you!

Ask each of them to think of a number between 1 and 5 and to write their numbers one beneath the other. Now ask them to add the two and write the total underneath. Now they must add that total to the number directly above it and write down the new total. They must continue adding the total to the number above it until they have a column of ten numbers. Now ask them to add up the whole column. You are bound to beat them to it, as you simply multiply the seventh number in the column by 11 to arrive at the correct answer!

Here is an example:

$$+ \quad 2$$
$$3$$
$$5$$
$$8$$
$$13$$
$$21$$
$$34 \times 11 = 374$$
$$55$$
$$89$$
$$\underline{144}$$
$$374$$

16

YAWNING

Everyone says that yawning is catching. Try it and see. One player yawns widely and everyone else tries not to. Sooner or later, some will give in. The winner is the last person to resist.

NATIONAL FLAGS

Just as America has the Stars and Stripes, and Britain has the Union Jack, so all countries have a national flag. Can you recognize these flags from their descriptions?

1. Blue, white and red vertical stripes.
2. A white cross on a red background.
3. Red, white and blue horizontal stripes.
4. A red circle on a white background.
5. A yellow cross on a blue background.
6. Green, white and red vertical stripes.

(Answers start on page 183.)

18

FISH FINGERS

Any number of players may join in this game. They all need a piece of cardboard and a sheet of newspaper.

The first task is for each person to cut a fish shape out of the piece of newspaper. Line up all the fish at one end of the room and race them to the other end. You may not touch the fish in any way at all. Just fan the sheet of cardboard to make a wind so that the fish flips and flaps its way along.

You could also play this game with just two fish, in the form of a team relay race.

QUEENIE

Play this game in a large field with lots of other players. One of you volunteers to be Queenie. She stands out in front with her back to the others, holding a ball. Queenie has to throw the ball over her shoulder to the other players and count to five. The players scramble to pick it up and one of them hides it behind him before Queenie shouts "five," and turns around. Queenie then has to guess which player has the ball. If she guesses wrong, she must throw again, but if she guesses right, the player holding the ball changes places with her.

20

ARTISTS

Write the letters of the alphabet onto pieces of paper and put them all in a box. Each player is provided with a sheet of drawing paper and a soft-tip pen. Everyone then picks a letter and has five minutes in which to draw a really good picture of something beginning with his or her letter.

Just as everyone does a drawing, so everyone joins in judging the best drawing.

GONE FISHING

You will need to do a little preparation for this game. Collect about twenty small flat pieces of wood or Styrofoam packing (at least three times as many pieces as there will be players). Write a number on one side in indelible ink and push a thumbtack into the other side. Half fill the bathtub with water and float all the pieces in it, thumbtacks facing upwards. Now, tie a magnet on the end of a string and tie the other end of the string to a stick, to make a fishing rod.

Let the players take turns fishing for three numbers. The winner is the player with the highest score.

22

FRENCH CRICKET

Play this game with a beach ball or other light ball and a baseball bat.

The batter holds the bat in both hands so that he can defend his legs below the knee from a direct hit from the ball. He may not move from the spot or even turn around. Other players form a circle around him and one player throws the ball, trying to hit his legs. If the batter misses, a player standing behind him can retrieve the ball and get in a quick throw before the batter is ready again.

The batter cannot be caught out; only a hit below the knee can make him hand the bat over to the bowler.

APPLE RINGS

September is the month for apple-picking, and while they are plentiful you could try this game. Peel an apple in one long strip, then throw the strip high into the air. It will fall on the floor in the shape of the initial letter of your future husband or wife's name.

24

HORSE

FEATHERS

This game is great fun but you need to be careful. Make sure that the "horse" you make is strong enough and very firm on the ground. Be careful also to use a good mattress under the pole so that no one is hurt if they fall.

First make the "horse." You need two sawhorses and a thick, 6-foot (2-m) long log or pole. Wrap the pole very well with sacking or similar material so that it is well padded. Then, lay the pole across the horses and tie it very firmly to them. If you think the horses may roll about once the riders have mounted, ask your friends to hold them firmly during play. Put a mattress on the ground under the pole.

Two riders now straddle the pole, facing each other and armed with a cushion or pillow. They gradually move nearer to each other, using the cushion to knock each other off the pole. A direct hit may dislodge one rider completely, but even if one little part of his body touches the ground or he hangs helplessly on the "horse" for ten seconds, he must still concede defeat. The winner meets the next challenger until everyone has had a go at it.

JOGGERS

This game, for teams or individuals, needs the help of several willing adults.

Everyone sets off from the start at one-minute intervals and jogs to point A—the tree at the end of the road, perhaps. Waiting there is an adult, who checks the time, gives the jogger a red ribbon, and tells him to jog to point B—a house on the next street, perhaps. Here the same procedure occurs and a different colored ribbon is handed out. So the game goes on until everyone has completed the course.

At the end, the time scores are added up and the team or person with the lowest time record wins—as long as he has collected a full set of ribbons.

26

HOW MANY SHADOWS?

Play this game when there are plenty of people about who can join in.

Blindfold a volunteer and stand him in the middle of the room. All the other players stand at one side of the room away from him. Now, use sign language to ask some of the other players to move quietly into position behind him. (They must stand close to him in order to give him a chance.) The blindfolded person must listen very carefully and guess how many shadows he has. If he guesses right, give him a prize and let someone else have a turn in the middle. If he guesses wrong, you could make him try again or make him forfeit.

LOADED DICE?

Tell your friend that if he throws the dice three times behind your back you will be able to tell him which numbers he threw.

Ask him to follow these instructions:

Throw the dice and multiply the number by 2.
Add 5
Multiply by 5
Throw the dice again and add on this number
Multiply by 10
Throw the dice again and add on this number
Tell you the result.

Now all you have to do is subtract 250 from the final number. You will be left with three figures, which will be the numbers thrown—in the order in which they came up.

28

BRIDGE QUIZ

America is a great country for bridges. Collect pictures and picture postcards—even photographs if you can—of six of the most famous bridges in the United States. Mount them on cardboard and test the general knowledge of any visitors to your house.

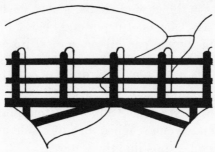

LADIES' NIGHT

Next time your parents are having a bonfire with all those fallen leaves in the yard, wait until the flames die down and try this little trick. Say the name of a person you think might be fond of you, then throw a hazelnut into the red-hot embers and say, "If you love me pop and fly, but if you don't then smoulder and die." Watch and see what "answer" you get.

30

ROCKS AND RAPIDS

Pretend your team is an exploration party that has just come to a fast-flowing river with rapids. There are rocks and reefs in the water and you have to climb over them to get across.

Set out a series of obstacles across the room. These are the reefs and rocks in the form of chairs, stools, cushions, boxes, upturned buckets, sheets of paper and board.

See how quickly you can all get across. No one may start until the last person is safely across and if a foot slips into the water (that is to say, touches the floor) that player scores 10 seconds in time faults.

Now time the next team. Add to the atmosphere by cheering wildly when anyone reaches the other side and by groaning loudly when he slips into the water.

OLOGIES

Lots of words end in "ology." See how many Ologies you can write down in ten minutes. They will be words like Geology, Biology, Anthropology, Apology, Anthology and Geomorphology. You should be able to think of at least twenty.

When you play this game with a friend, compare lists and explain any new words to each other.

2

NUMBER
STORY

A large house or yard is a "must" for this team game. Work out a route all around it, up and down hallways, in and out of rooms, around trees, over flowerbeds, and so on. Each team should have about six members, but you can have as many teams as you like. Each team has a leader and the other members each has a number.

Give each leader a copy of a story prepared beforehand. It may read like this: "When we got to camp we saw at once there was only ONE tree standing. We ran down to the pool to see THREE logs across it. The high fence had been broken and FIVE posts were missing. We made a rapid survey of the area and found TWO water troughs were gone. By now it was FOUR o'clock. . . ."

When the leaders read the story out loud, the players must leap up as soon as they hear their number and race around the circuit. The first complete team home wins.

WHOSE WALK?

Can you recognize your friends by the way they walk? Try this and find out.

Cut armholes and eyeholes in an old sheet. Now send half of the players out of the room. One of them must come back—barefoot, and wearing the sheet. He or she should try to disguise his walk as he moves around the room. Do you know who it is?

4

FALL COLLECTION

Keep your eyes open when you're on a country walk and collect as many different seedpods or berries as you can. Back at home, mount them on a cardboard and see how many of them you and the family can identify. Do you know which trees or bushes they all come from?

5

HOPPING AND CHARGING

Divide the players into two teams and, starting with the biggest member of each team, give each one a number.

All players stand in a large circle, then, when the umpire calls out a number, the two players holding that number have to hop into the middle on one leg, arms folded, and try to knock each other off balance. The first one to fall over or put both feet on the ground is the loser and another number is called. Play on soft grass or piles of leaves to soften any falls.

The umpire must make sure everyone has a turn and can end by calling several numbers at once, just for fun.

6

WILDLIFE QUIZ—PRAIRIES

Can you list these ten animals and birds which are to be found in the lake and prairie regions of North America?

1. Whitetail
2. Meadow
3. Black
4. Starnose
5. Chimney
6. Eastern
7. — lark
8. Striped
9. Indigo
10. — cottontail

(Answers start on page 183.)

7

MAIN STREET QUIZ

How much do you know about your town, city, suburb, neighborhood? Perhaps you have a Main Street or a long boulevard, or a mixture of stores, churches, garages, and so on. Taking, say, a mile in each direction from both sides of the main road, how many places can you list from memory?

Try drawing a map, with a friend, and marking all the places on it that you remember. Now go for a walk together and see how many places you had right and how many you forgot.

TASTE BUDS

Prepare a number of small saucers or plates with samples of table salt, rock salt, honey, vinegar, olive oil, various jams and jellies, peanut butter, mint chocolate, mint sauce, finely-chopped onions, kitchen flavoring essences, etc. Blindfold a friend and let him or her dip a finger in each saucer and guess the taste.

9

GHOSTS

What could be better than a ghostly game for a dark autumn evening? Ask everyone to pick a folded piece of paper from a hat. One paper bears the letter G for Ghost, another the letter E for Exorcist, and all the rest are blank.

Now the lights are turned off. The Exorcist stays where he is, but the Ghost gets up and sends his icy fingers up and down someone's spine. The victim counts to ten, giving the Ghost time to get away, and then screams. The lights go back on and it is up to the Exorcist to question everyone and so find the Ghost. The Ghost can lie as much as he likes, but everyone else must tell the truth.

HIDDEN FRUIT

Here are five fruits in rhyming clues. When you have found them the initial letters of each fruit will make the name of yet another one to make six in all.

1. Most of the spring month is needed here,
    As you write the fruit begins to appear.

2. A coniferous tree you now must find,
    With the fruit Adam tasted coming behind.

3. You could reap a rich fruit harvest here,
    Unravel a word and the fruit will appear.

4. The color of the fruit to change. . .
    The melon you must rearrange.

5. Not a new berry it's very clear,
    A more senior one is needed here!

(Answers start on page 183.)

11
TAILWAGGERS

Tailwaggers wear a simple belt into which a handkerchief, light-colored scarf, or length of ribbon or tape is tucked firmly at the back. If belts are difficult to get, then use the same tails tucked firmly into jeans, skirts, or whatever.

    Ask the players to get into pairs. Each player has to try and steal the other's tail while defending his own. Any winner may challenge any other winner until a champion tailwagger is found.

12
RUOK?

RUOK, when read as single letters and not as a word, sounds like "Are you okay?" Have a competition to see who can make the longest list of words that sound like letters of the alphabet. "Enemy" sounds like NME. "See if you" sounds like CFU. Allow plenty of thinking time for this game.

13

WITCH'S
BROOM

This is another game which isn't really competitive but is great fun to let off steam.

Ask everyone to form a circle, facing inwards and looking down, with their hands behind their backs. Now, walk around the outside of the circle, carrying two tightly rolled newspapers. These are the brooms. Put one broom into one of the players' hands. This is then the "witch." The "witch" immediately starts whacking the person to his right on his seat. The one being whacked must race around the circle, pursued by the witch, trying to get back into position before he is hit too many times.

If you can do it quickly enough, put the second newspaper into the hands of the person to the left of the first witch, so that he too is being whacked and three people in all are chasing around the circle.

PICK UP STICKS

In the fall when there are plenty of twigs on the ground among the fallen leaves, go out and collect an armful, all about 2 feet (60 cm) long. You also need six forked sticks and one very long stick with a hook or curve at one end. (Put this last one to one side.)

Hold the sticks in a bundle in your arms and drop them on the floor, keeping your feet well out of the way. The first player now uses the curved stick to lift one of the sticks off the pile. If he does this without making any of the others move, he keeps it and has another turn. If another one moves, he must leave them all where they are and hand the curved stick over to the next player.

At the end of the game, each player scores 5 points for each forked stick and one for each of the others.

15

INDIAN LEG WRESTLING

Try a contest of strength with a friend. Lie down side by side with your head at his or her feet. Each raises the right leg and hooks the other person behind the knee. Make sure this grip is correctly held. *Using the leg only*, each player must try to turn the other over onto his or her side.

TELEGRAMS

This game will test your ingenuity, and give you a chance to say what you think about your friends, but don't be nasty because they will be saying something about you, too!

Take each person's name from a group of friends. Now you all have to make up a telegram, using words which begin with the letters of the name in the right order. The telegram must also have something to do with the actual person. Say your name is Peter and you are good at games, then one of the telegrams about you could be: "Previous Endeavors Tiring Entertainment Required."

17

RED HOT POKER

Choose any object you like to be the Red Hot Poker. A dog's artificial bone made of rubber or plastic is an ideal shape for passing around, but almost any kind of toy will do instead. You also need a plastic or enamel plate to spin.

Players should sit in a circle and pass the Poker around the circle very rapidly. One player sets the plate spinning in the middle of the circle. Any player caught with the Red Hot Poker when the plate stops spinning is out.

Instead of a plate, you could use an alarm clock. Do not be caught holding the Poker when the ringing stops!

CHANGING TREES

Have you noticed how the same tree can look quite different at different times of the year? Collect tree pictures from magazines, or make your own drawings from a reference book. Show some as winter skeletons, some in full leaf in summer, and some in their autumn colors. Include a couple of trees more than once, but from different seasons, just to confuse everyone.

    Mount all the pictures on a poster for your room and then use it as the basis for an identification quiz when friends come to visit.

19

HUNTING
HALLOWEEN

The two weeks between October 18 (St. Luke's Summer or Indian Summer) and October 31 (Halloween) were used by the Indians as a great preparation time for winter, when enormous buffalo hunts took place to lay in stocks of winter meat. So why not send your friends off "hunting"?

    First, plan out a course covering about a mile (kilometre). Divide the players into teams and give each one a length of rope. They have to tie the rope into a circle, all get inside it and race around the course making suitable hunting cries. The winning team is the one with the fastest time and the rope circle still intact.

20
FIBBER

Play this card game with four players. Shuffle and deal all the cards so that each player has the same number. Players may look at the cards in their hands. Now they take turns laying a card face down in the middle of the table. The first player calls "one" as he does so, the second "two," and so on, right through jack, queen and king and back to one again. But it is up to them whether they *really* put down the card they are naming.

If any player calls out "Fibber" to the one laying the card, he must turn it over and show whether he was telling the truth. If it was a lie, he must pick up all the cards from the table. If it was the truth, the challenger must pick up the cards. The winner is the first player to get rid of all his cards.

21
SCRUMPING

"Scrumping" is an old English word for stealing apples.

To play this game, everyone stands in a circle and an apple is placed in the middle. One player is named the Thief and must leave the room until called back. While the Thief is out of the room, select someone in the circle to be the Farmer. When the Thief returns, he or she must prowl about the circle and eventually try to snatch the apple from the middle of the circle and run out of the room with it. The Farmer dashes in as soon as the snatch is made, and does his or her best to stop the theft. The Thief has no idea who the Farmer is before he tries his grab and getaway.

NURSERY RHYME QUIZ

Do you have a long memory? If so, can you remember any nursery rhymes? Here are the initial letters of the first few words of ten of them.

1. MMQCHDYGG
2. BBBSHYAW
3. HDDTCATFTCJOTM
4. TBMTBMSHTRSHTR
5. LTHSIACEHCP
6. MHALLIFWWAS
7. LBBCBYHTSITMTCITC
8. HDSOAWHDHAGF
9. OKCWAMOSAAMOSWH
10. SASOSAPFOR

(Answers start on page 183.)

23

WOLFISH WORD GAME

The key word in this game is WOLFISHLY. Can you find 28 or more words in it? The rules are simple. Words must be of four or more letters. Plurals are not permitted. Proper names, either Christian or surnames, are not used. The average score for "Wolfishly" is 24 words found in 30 minutes.

(Answers start on page 183.)

WHAT RHYME THIS TIME?

Here is a quiet thinking game to show which of you are on the same wavelength.

One player says "I'm thinking of a word, and it rhymes with DOG." All the others have to guess. It could be Bog, Cog, Fog, Agog, Hog, Jog, Log, Tog, or any word that rhymes.

Try some more difficult examples like FAME or CHAIR. Some words, like CARPET, will be almost impossible.

25

THROW THE DICE

All players write down the numbers 1 through 12 on a piece of paper, then take turns throwing two dice. Each player throws the dice once for his turn, unless both dice show the same number on the first throw when he is allowed a second throw.

After each throw, the player adds up the total number of spots on the dice and crosses that number off his list. If he throws a double, he can cross off the number 1, if he wishes, instead of throwing the dice a second time. The winner is the first player to cross off all the numbers on his list.

TAP THE BALLOON

Ask all the players to sit in a circle. One of them puts a balloon into the air, at the same time saying the name of the person he is sending it to. While it is in the air, the second person names the player he will be sending it to, and then taps it in that direction. The ball must be kept in the air the whole time. If it's dropped or tapped in the wrong direction, that player collects a minus point.

The player with the least number of minus points at the end of the game is the winner.

27

FLYING FLOUNDER

Compete with a friend to see who can manage the most flying flounders.

One person must lie on the ground, legs stretched out behind, and raise himself up as if walking on his hands. The other person must stand between his legs and pick him up around the thighs.

The idea is for the first person to spring up like a flying flounder with his arms stretched out to the sides. (The holder helps with a strong upwards heave.)

See how many spring-ups you can manage without stopping.

SCISSORS, PAPER, STONE

In this game for two players, the hand is used to represent scissors (first and second fingers extended in a V-shape; thumb, ring and little fingers bent under), or paper (open hand) or stone (clenched fist).

Each player holds one hand behind his back and forms it into scissors, paper or stone. You now count "one, two, three" and simultaneously, on the count of three, show the hands and compare them. Score like this: Both hands the same—a draw. Scissors and paper—scissors score one point because they cut paper. Stone and paper—paper scores one point because it wraps stone. Stone and scissors—stone scores one point because it blunts scissors. The winner is the player with the highest score after 15 rounds.

29

WRIST WRESTLERS

For this game you need an opponent and an umpire. Play this game on soft grassy ground or a pile of fallen leaves to soften the falls.

Lie down on the ground facing your opponent, and raise yourself on your toes and hands, keeping your body and elbows straight. Your opponent must do the same.

When the umpire shouts "Go," try to snatch one of your opponent's wrists from under him and make him bite the dust! But beware. As soon as you raise one hand to attack, he may well strike at your other wrist.

MONSTERS

At the end of October is Halloween, the time for fancy dress parties. Ask everyone to come dressed as a witch, a wizard, or some kind of monster.

The traditional Halloween game is apple-bobbing. Float several apples in a bucket of water and ask your guests to take out one each—using only their mouths.

31
SPIRITS

Halloween also happens to be the last night of the Celtic Year, so here is a suitably spooky game from Wales to play on October 31.

Everyone sits around a table by candlelight, holding hands tightly all the way around, elbows resting on the table. The Chief Druid (someone of Welsh ancestry, if possible) moans loudly: "The spirit moves us, brothers and sisters, the shock wave is moving through us. . . ." Tension rises at once and the shock wave goes around the circle more than once. Doors and windows bang, owls hoot, there is the noise of crying, a man talks mysteriously in French. . . . It is amazing what you can do with an accomplice and a tape recorder outside the door!

PLOW HORSES

Lay out a course of obstacles along the ground—tree trunks, large stones, piles of leaves, coats, and so on. Now blindfold someone who is to be a "Horse" and tie a rope loosely to each of his or her wrists. The "Plowman" must walk along behind the horse, guiding it through the obstacles. He is not allowed to speak and can only pull the left-hand rope to make the Horse go to the left, the right-hand rope to make it go to the right, and both together to make it stop or start. Each Plowman starts the course with ten points, but loses one point each time his Horse touches an obstacle.

Let everyone have a try as both Horse and Plowman.

2

POT BLACK

For this game you need three table tennis balls and an assortment of plastic containers—bowls, buckets, flowerpots, anything you like. One of the containers should be black. Chalk a number on each one, the black container having the highest score, which is 10.

The first player should stand at the other end of the room and throw one of the balls so that it bounces towards the pots and—hopefully—into one of them. After three throws, the score is added up and the next player has a turn.

Needless to say, the idea is to aim for the black pot, which has the highest score.

OVER THE
SHOULDER

Play this game indoors on gym mats or out-of-doors on sand or soft grass.

Players should stand back to back, hands and shoulders touching and arms by the sides, with fingers interlinked.

Each person must push and shove and bend and twist in an effort to tip his opponent over his shoulder.

4

SPORTS JARGON

Every sport, hobby, game or pastime has its own jargon. What would you be doing if you were . . .
1. Jumping the gun
2. Throwing in the towel
3. Dribbling the ball
4. Working a fly
5. Potting the black
6. Hole in one
7. 30:40
8. Catching a crab

(Answers start on page 183.)

THE SUSPENSION GAME

The Suspension Game never fails to cause a lot of interest in a program of games and stunts. Just keep it handy for any occasion and spectators might actually ask you for your autograph!

Do you think it is possible to hang a lady's ring on a string of common salt? No? Amaze your friends by telling them that you can do it. Then show them all how it is done.

Prepare the salt first. Take a short length of thread and soak it in a *very strong* solution of common salt. After 30 to 40 minutes take the thread out and allow it to dry. Add more salt, and soak the thread again for 30 minutes. Repeat the process four more times. Take the thread out for the sixth time and let it dry completely. It will be coated with white salt crystals. Slide the ring onto the thread and hang it up. Have an adult light the thread with a match. It will burn away quickly, leaving the ring suspended on salt alone.

6

UMBRELLA

OBSTACLES

Lay out an obstacle race around a lawn or field, with all manner of things to climb over, under or around. Contestants, who are timed by an umpire, must move around the course at a fast walk with an egg in a spoon in one hand and an open umbrella in the other.

This can be more difficult than it sounds, particularly on a windy day. Avoid too much expense by using a hard-boiled egg.

COIN IN THE BUCKET

Mark a cross on each side of a dime with a crayon and then drop the dime into a bucket of water. Ask all your friends to drop in a dime and try to make theirs land on top of yours. If anyone succeeds, he takes all of them. If no one succeeds, you could be kind and give them all their money back.

8

MONSTER
PROBLEMS

Read out these puzzles to your friends and see if anyone can give you the correct answer. Read each puzzle once, slowly and clearly, and do not repeat anything. Let them jot down figures if they wish.

1) Multiply eight by three, add two dozen, subtract six, multiply by two, add eleven, add five, divide by ten, multiply by eleven, subtract a dozen, add two and divide by ten. What is the answer?

2) Divide twenty-seven by nine, add thirty, divide by eleven, add a century, add two hundred, take away three, multiply by a hundred, take away twenty-nine thousand, divide by four, add fifty and divide by thirty. What is the answer?

(Answers start on page 183.)

MISSING ADJECTIVES

Adjectives are words which describe things—"red," "big," "smelly," "exciting" are all adjectives. For this game, read aloud a paragraph from one of your books, but instead of reading the adjectives, say the word "blank." It might go like this: "Once upon a time there lived a blank girl called Goldilocks, who lived in a blank house on the edge of a blank blank forest."

Read your paragraph very slowly so that your audience can try to write down the words that they think you replaced with blanks. Then read out the true version. Will anyone have all the blanks filled in correctly?

10

ODD ONE OUT

Who or what is the odd one out? Try this quiz yourself and then test your friends.

1) Ilie Nastase, Bjorn Borg, Joe Greene, Jimmy Connors.
2) Jack Nicklaus, Gary Player, Hale Irwin, Steve Cauthen.
3) Joe Frazier, Mario Andretti, Jody Scheckter, James Hunt.

Try making up other sets of people, places or things with an odd one out.

(Answers start on page 183.)

SILENT LETTER

This game for two or more players can go on for a week, if you want it to. Decide on any letter—start with a consonant—and ban it from your conversation. Avoid using the word yourself, but try to trick others into using it. Score a minus point every time the word is used, and the person with the lowest score at the end of the game—or week!—is the winner.

12

LISTENING POST

When bad weather keeps you indoors, a listening game can take the place of more boisterous activities.

Find a record or tape, if you can, of wild bird songs. These are often available from libraries, record shops, and conservation societies. Sit everyone down with a pencil and paper and get them to write down the names of the birds making the calls. The first time you do this, very few people will get the right answers, but after a while you will all be surprised at how many you can recognize.

REPTILES QUIZ

How much do you know about these cold-blooded animals which many people seem to find unpleasant? Here are the names of eight reptiles—with the vowels removed. Do you still recognize them?

1. GNT TRTS
2. CHMLN
3. CRCDL
4. GN
5. BSLSK
6. GCK
7. B CNSTRCTR
8. SLMNDR

(Answers start on page 183.)

14

HOPBALL

For Hopball you need a small playing area with a simple goal at either end. Each goal is just a space between two logs or large stones. You play with two teams of three players each and use a softball or small football. Play for two minutes each way.

A referee starts the game by dropping the ball to the ground, with the players standing around him in a circle. Now each team, hopping on one foot and kicking the ball with the other, tries to score into their opponents' goal.

15   November

CATCH
A
SHOOTING
STAR

From now until November 19 and from December 8−15 are the times when you are most likely to see "shooting stars," or meteors. A meteor is a piece of matter from outer space which burns up when it enters the earth's atmosphere. It generally looks like a bright star moving across the sky.

Dress warmly and go out stargazing with some friends. Who will spot the first shooting star?

16

ALPHABET PICTURE

Look in an old magazine for two full-page pictures that are crammed with lots of different things. Cut the pictures out, turn both face down on the table, and ask a friend to choose one. You take the other, and both pick up a pair of scissors. Cut out an object from your picture beginning with the letter A, then one beginning with B, and then C. See which of you can get the nearest to a complete set of 26.

BLINDFOLD STAG

In this game, one player is the Stag and the other is the Stalker, and both are well blindfolded. The one basic rule is that both players must at all times have some part of the body making contact with a table. If contact is lost, that player is automatically out.

The game starts with the Stag at one end and the Stalker at the other. The Stag is captured if he or she is firmly grasped and the blindfold removed, but if the Stag evades capture for three minutes, he or she wins. Let everybody have a go at playing both characters.

18 November

BUSTER

This is a game of strength for two people of equal size, weight and height. They should stand facing each other on either side of a marked line, and then stretch their arms out wide and grasp each other's hands. Chins are rested on each other's shoulders. Now, keeping the arms strictly wide out at all times, each person attempts to push the other over the line, pushing only with his chest.

BALANCING CONTEST

For this game you need an empty bottle (a wine bottle will do) and a large box of toothpicks. See how many toothpicks you can balance across the neck of the bottle, adding one at a time. Every time they fall off, you must start again, until you feel you have reached a record figure. Now hand the bottle and toothpicks over to a friend and see if he or she can beat your record.

20

TICK-TOCK

Ask a volunteer to leave the room and while he or she is away, move the furniture around a little to make things a bit more difficult. Put away anything that might break or be dangerous to walk into. Then hide an alarm clock (the louder the tick, the better) in a wastepaper basket, or perhaps behind the curtains—somewhere not too easy to find.

Now call back the volunteer who has been blindfolded. With only the ticking to guide him, he must start looking for the clock. All the others should keep quiet unless he looks as if he might bump into something hard, then they can shout out a warning.

Take turns being blindfolded and see who can find the clock in the shortest time.

THE BUTTON GAME

Can you read minds? To find out, all you need are half a dozen buttons and a few friends.

Ask all of your friends except one to stand in a line with their hands behind their backs. When you go out of the room, the extra player must walk along the line, putting a button into six of the hands. The players are now allowed to pass the buttons from one hand to another.

When they have stopped and are holding out clenched fists in front of them, you can come back and start mind-reading to see which hands are holding the buttons. Use all the clues! Some people find it hard to suppress a grin if they are holding one or more buttons. Others have white knuckles or a particular look in their eyes.

You are allowed three guesses and then it is someone else's turn.

22

MAGIC PEPPER

Mix up some salt and pepper with a spoon, then challenge your audience to separate them again. Does anyone know how? When they admit defeat, rub the spoon briskly against your sweater, then hold it just above the mixture. The pepper, being lighter than the salt, will be attracted by static electricity and will rise to the spoon.

TAP-TAP-TAP

Mark out a large circle on the floor which all the players must stay inside. One of the players is given a short stick to tap, tap, tap on the ground, without raising it more than six inches (15 cm).

The aim of the stick-tapper is to tap lightly as many players as possible on the ankle (they are then "out") while tapping the stick constantly on the floor. The players can only *walk* to avoid him.

The last player to be tapped takes over as the tapper.

24

COLDITZ

Colditz was a German prison in the Second World War. It is famous for the stories of British soldiers who escaped from there. If you enjoyed playing "Capture the Castle" (August 5), then try this one which is exactly the opposite.

One team of five or six people must link arms tightly in a circle to make Colditz Castle. Inside the circle are the members of the other team, who must try their hardest to get out.

Ask an umpire to decide which team makes the fastest escape.

STEPPING STONES

This is a team game in which you have to use your imagination. First of all, mark out a wide river with two long ropes (or lengths of garden hose, if you're playing outdoors).

Now, the members of both teams gather on one river bank, each holding two small sheets of newspaper which act as stepping stones. All the members of the team have to cross the river without getting their feet wet. At the word "Go," the first member of each team puts his or her stepping stone into the river and steps on it. Then he places the second stepping stone ahead and steps on that before retrieving the first stone.

As soon as the first team member arrives on the other side, the second sets off, and so on. The winning team is the one that crosses in the fastest time, with five seconds being added every time a team member gets a foot wet (by stepping in the river *without* stepping on a paper).

26

STATUES

If you are out for a walk with some friends, take turns shouting commands. Wait for the moment everyone least suspects it, then shout "Freeze." All must stop immediately and adopt a striking pose. Anyone who moves, laughs, or talks is out immediately. The winner is the player who can keep up his or her pose the longest with the most perfect deadpan expression.

Now continue with the walk until the next person shouts.

TRAPBALL

One of the skills to master in soccer is the art of trapping a moving ball with the feet to kill it dead. This game makes use of that skill.

Players form a circle with one of them in the middle. A standard-sized football or volleyball is rolled rapidly across the circle from one player to another, passing close by the player in the middle. The ball must be kept moving quickly and the player in the middle must stay where he is, trying to trap the ball dead as it passes by. Each player has three minutes in the middle and the one who succeeds in stopping the ball the most times, wins.

28

TRADE NAMES

Your surname may come from the job an ancestor did. Hand out papers and pencils and see who can make the longest list of trade names that are also surnames.

Here are some examples to start you off: Butcher, Cooper (barrel-maker), Gardener, Taylor, Tiler, Drover, Wayman (weighman), Carpenter.

29

"REVOKING" QUIZ

How many words of four or more letters can you make from
the word REVOKING?

(Answers start on page 183.)

30

SLEEPING INDIAN

One person sits, blindfolded, in the middle of the room. He is
the Sleeping Indian. All the others sit in a wide circle around
him and one of them is chosen to be the leader. The Sleeping
Indian has a bunch of keys at his feet and lies down, pretend-
ing to be asleep.

Now, the leader points to another member of the circle who
then crawls, as quietly as possible, towards the Sleeping
Indian. He must try and pick up the keys and return to his
position without being heard. If he is challenged, the leader
must point to someone else to have a try but if he is successful, he then changes places with the Sleeping Indian. The
Sleeping Indian then takes over the leader's part so that
everyone has a chance of being the Sleeping Indian and the
leader as well.

SWIPE

Ask every player to take any object he or she likes and place it in the middle of the room. The objects can be anything at all as long as they are not too big. Now, remove one article. Everybody then starts jogging around the outside of the room in a follow-the-leader style. You can have tape music or a cassette playing. When the music suddenly stops, everybody dashes to the heap in the middle and swipes an article. One article has been removed, so there is one player who doesn't get a swipe and must drop out. And so it goes on, an item removed after each round, until there is a winner.

2

BLIND

BALANCE

Stretch a long ribbon, tape or gauze bandage across the floor and weigh it down at each end. Get the first player to take off his shoes and socks, then blindfold him, put two books on his head, and start him off along the tape, pointing him in the right direction.

The idea is to walk the length of the tape without either dropping the books (penalty five points) or straying off the line (penalty one point). Bystanders are allowed to call out instructions to guide the player back to the line if he leaves it, but each time that happens he loses a point.

The winner is the player with the lowest number of points after three tries.

SHOES
FOR
ALL

For this game the players must divide into two teams and all take off their shoes. Shoes from each team are jumbled up and put in a box, one box at each side of the umpire.

The umpire then takes a shoe from each box and throws them at the same time towards the teams. The shoe owners leap up and put on their shoes as quickly as possible. As soon as a shoe is on the right foot, the umpire throws another one from that team's box.

If this is too easy, try the game in almost total darkness, using a small flashlight in each team's "camp" to spotlight the shoes as they're thrown.

4
SLIPPERY SOAP

Try this game on an icy playground after thick frost or snow. Mark out a long thin course. About 15 yards (13.5 m) from the base line draw five numbered boxes one yard square (1 m), one behind the other. Stand on the base line and compete with a friend to slide a large cake of bath soap along the course, trying to land in the box with the highest number. Make the soap slippery in a bucket of water to see if it will slide further.

PUZZLING POEM

Try this riddle.

My first is in hedge whether brown or green,
My second in oak but not in keen,
My third is in larch and also in light,
My fourth is in lime but not in might,
My last is in yew yet not in wed,
. . . And I am a tree with berries red.

(Answers start on page 183.)

6

STUMP SPEECHES

Play this game while gathered around a fire on a cold evening. Ask everyone to write down a subject of topical or amusing interest and put it into a hat. When this is done, shake the hat well, and let the first person draw a piece of paper. He or she must immediately talk on this subject, without hesitation, repetition or deviation, for one minute. Challenges can be made for all these faults; if a challenge is correct, the speaker drops out and the next player pulls a subject out of the hat.

MYSTERY TAPES

For this you need two teams of about four players each and two tape recorders. Ask the teams to record, during the next week, any unusual sounds they hear. On a given day, they all get together to listen to each other's tapes and see how many sounds they can guess.

8

WHAT TREE AM I?

When everyone is feeling quite silly at a party, ask them all to pick the name of a tree and then take turns miming it for the others to guess.

They must show if it is tall and strong or thin and willowy, shady or spreading, deciduous or coniferous.

You will be surprised at how many trees will be guessed correctly. Now mime one yourself. Just stand still and point to someone. You are a yew ("you") tree, of course!

BALL IN THE NET

Try this game with four people playing in pairs. Each pair needs a stick with a curve at the end, a tennis ball net, and six tennis balls. Tie or tape the net to the end of the stick so that it forms a bag that hangs open.

One of the pair holds the tennis balls and the other, standing 8 feet (2.5 m) away, attempts to catch the balls in his net. When all six balls have been thrown, the thrower must rush and pick up any that were missed, go back to the marker, and try again.

Set a time limit of three minutes before seeing who has caught the most balls.

10

TEN!

This is a game to play with used matchsticks. Your friends will puzzle for hours over it, and groan when they see the answer. But first you have a go and see if you can guess the catch.

This is what you do. Lay four matches side by side with about a matchstick's space between them. Now add five more matchsticks to make ten!

(Answers start on page 183.)

FROM A TO ZA

If you see the letters USA on the back of a race car, you know
it stands for United States of America. And if you see GB, you
probably know it stands for Great Britain.

But do you know which countries these letters stand for?
Try them yourself then test your friends.

1. A	12. L
2. B	13. MEX
3. CH	14. N
4. D	15. PL
5. ET	16. RA
6. FL	17. S
7. GR	18. TR
8. H	19. U
9. IL	20. V
10. J	21. Y
11. K	22. ZA

(Answers start on page 183.)

12

PARTY CHAINS

Why not have a paper-chain-making contest between either
individuals or teams? Hand out scissors, glue and colored
paper and, after half an hour, see who has the largest chain.

FAMOUS ADVERTISEMENTS

This is a Miming game, best done in twos and threes as television advertisements usually feature more than one person. Each team gets together in advance and prepares an ad completely in mime. Then, on party night, you all have a chance to guess what everyone else's advertisement is.

14

HOW LONG DO THEY LIVE?

How long do you think is the average life of these animals? Try to link up the animals in the first list with the life spans in the second.

1. Elephant
2. Man
3. Mayfly
4. Parrot
5. Ostrich
6. Tortoise

A. 24 hours
B. 60 years
C. 152 years
D. 50 years
E. 70 years
F. 26 years

(Answers start on page 183.)

BLOW FOOTBALL

For this game you need a rectangular table slightly smaller than a table tennis table. Mark the half-way line and a middle point with chalk, and use shoe boxes or similar-sized boxes as goals. For each player (three on a side is best) you need a 9-inch (22.5-cm) length of narrow metal or plastic tubing.

Position the players around the table—two on each side and one at each end to act as goalkeepers—and set a table tennis ball on the middle line.

At the word "Go," players attempt to blow the ball into the other team's goal. If the ball is blown off the table, then a "blow-in" is awarded to the other side.

Play five minutes each way.

16

MUSICAL CHAIRS

Everyone knows the old game of musical chairs, using a line of chairs facing alternate ways. Everyone walks around the chairs, and when the music stops they have to grab a chair and sit down. Anyone without a chair is out, and every time the game re-starts, one chair is removed.

Here are some variations to try:
1) blindfold all the players;
2) use an assortment of seats—chairs, armchairs, kitchen stools, cushions;
3) the players go around in pairs and sit down with one on the other's knee.

17

SNOW SNAKE

This is an adaptation of an Iroquois Indian game. Find a long, gentle slope on a snow-covered hillside and build a course running downhill by packing the snow down hard and "polishing" it as well as you can. Now, find a stick the same height as yourself and throw it, like a low-flying javelin, down the channel.

Whose stick travels the farthest? Leave a marker at the champion's distance and try again.

18

PATIENCE IN FOURS

A game of Patience is just the thing for long winter evenings. This is a very simple game that can last for weeks—if you have the patience.

Shuffle a pack of cards and deal 4 cards, face up, placing them side by side *from left to right*. If the numbers or pictures on any of the cards are the same, put them all on the same pile, moving them across *from left to right*. Deal a second set of four cards on top of the first, and again move any that are the same. If, when you move a card, it uncovers one that is the same as one on the top of another pile, move them together in the same way. Continue to deal the cards in fours. When the pack is used up, pick up the piles *from right to left*. Put the right-hand pile on top of the one next to it. Then pick up the whole of that pile and move it to the left onto the pile next to it, and so on. Turn over the whole pile and start again.

When four identical cards appear in a line, one on top of each pile, you may remove them from the game. Eventually, you will have none left—if you are lucky.

THE SOUNDS GAME

This game is best played using a screen with the players sitting on the opposite side *with their backs* to it. If you have no screen, sit behind a partly open door instead. All players should have notebooks and pencils and write down what sounds they think are being made and how they are being made.

  Try these for a start:

Pour small stones from a height of about two feet (60 cm) into a plastic bucket.
Stretch an elastic band and start twanging on it musically.
Play a simple tune on glasses of water with the water at differing levels, using a small wooden spoon or spatula.
Wind an alarm clock.
Burst a few balloons. (Easy? Then how many balloons?)
Rattle a bunch of keys . . . how many keys?
Play something on a harmonica . . . name the tune.
Play a tape recording of someone sawing wood, using a sewing machine, and so on.

  This is much more difficult than it sounds, and some of the answers are sure to be rather strange.

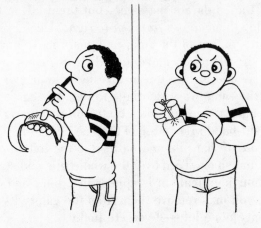

MIXED QUESTIONS

Use a stopwatch or a watch with a second hand to see how quickly you can answer these jumbled-up questions. Just write down the answers, not the questions themselves. Now challenge a friend to break your record.

1. Cats birds walk four do or on legs?
2. Capital England is Manchester the London of or?
3. Clock what midnight does strike a at?
4. Christmas in month what is?
5. Wheels many bicycle how a has?
6. Smokers what put pipes do their in?
7. Animals provide what bacon?
8. Pens with fountain what you fill do?

(Answers start on page 183.)

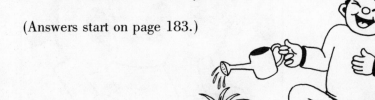

21

ACT THE WORD

This is a good indoor game for the cold weather and it tests your acting skill!

Choose one of your friends and send him out of the room while the others decide on an adverb, like angrily, gracefully or laughingly. Now, call your victim back inside. He asks the others in turn to perform some task, each in the manner of the word that has been chosen. Once he has guessed the word, send someone else outside and begin the game again.

WINTER

On this, the shortest day of the year, see if you can make 17 new words from the word WINTER. Each word must contain four or more letters.

(Answers start on page 183.)

23

ANIMAL CAROL

Now that carols are in the air, here's a game where you can have fun making up new words—and singing them as well.

Ask everyone to sit in a circle. Now start with "On the first day of Christmas, my true love sent to me . . ." and then add something to do with animals, like "a parrot sitting on a dog." The next person has to repeat your line and add the second one, for example, "On the second day of Christmas my true love sent to me two tiny turtles and a parrot sitting on a dog." The next person repeats what has gone before and adds a third, and so on. Try to make the whole thing sound really ridiculous.

PASS THE—WHAT?

Ask all the players to sit around a table and then put the lights out. Now hand them six objects, one by one, which they have to pass around from one person to the next until all objects come back to you. When the lights go on again, they have to write down the six objects in the correct order.

Use a variety of objects such as an orange, a banana, a potato, a walnut, and even something nasty like a peeled grape.

25

CELEBRITIES

If a party is planned for Christmas afternoon, this game will make an excellent ice-breaker.

Prepare in advance a set of cards, each bearing the name of a celebrity. Pin one on the back of each guest and remind them as you do so that *no one* may read any of the names out loud.

The players can now try to discover which name is on their backs by asking questions such as "Am I alive or dead?" "If I'm very old, what century did I live in?" "Do I feature in the Bible?" "Do my legs make me famous?" and many more. Once they guess the name, the card is removed.

The last person left in the room with a card on his back is the loser.

FIND THE MATCHBOX

Divide the players into two teams and blindfold one person from each. Place two chairs at the other end of the room, with an empty matchbox on each. The blindfolded players now have to go and pick up a matchbox and bring it back to their team, who are allowed to shout out helpful instructions.

The first player to bring back a matchbox wins a point for the team. Carry on until everyone has had a turn with the blindfold.

27

WHO AM I?

Winter is the season for coughs and colds, so in case you have to stay in bed for a day or two, here is a thinking game for when friends come to visit.

One person chooses a famous character from a book, fairy tale, play, film or television series, and must answer questions just as that person would. The other players must ask questions and try to guess who the character is.

Can you guess from these questions and answers the name of the character?

Q. What did you do today?

A. I went to visit my grandmother and had a very nasty experience.

Q. Where does your grandmother live?

A. In a wood.

Q. What is your favorite color?

A. Red. I often wear it.

The first person to guess the character's name (Little Red Riding Hood in this case) gets the chance to be the next mystery character.

DOG
SHOW

Visit any store selling picture postcards of dogs and buy a varied collection of breeds. Number each one, then trim off all identifying matter from the photo. Make sure you keep a list of all the breed names against the relevant numbers. Prop up the cards around the room.

Give other members of the family a pencil and paper and ask them to write down the names of the breeds in a given time limit.

29

ODD MAN OUT

Can you spot which are the odd men out?

1. Flute, clarinet, viola, bassoon, piccolo.
2. Squash, tennis, baseball, darts, table tennis.
3. Ragout, minestrone, moussaka, meringue, kebab.
4. Tango, pirouette, quickstep, waltz, foxtrot, black bottom.
5. Monkey, mongoose, tiger, elephant, mammal.
6. Lapland, Canada, Zambia, Germany, Egypt, France.

(Answers start on page 183.)

CROSS OUT THE "A'S"

You will need several copies of the same edition of a news-paper, one for each player. Give each person a ballpoint pen and ask them to cross out all the letter A's they can find on a given page, as well as all the words "and" and "at."

Stop them after ten minutes—or earlier if anyone finishes the page sooner—and get them to swap papers and award a point for all the correct crossings out. Deduct a point for any skipped over. The winner is the one with the most total points.

31

PUSH THE BUTTON

This table-top game is played by two people using thirteen buttons which are identical in shape and size or with poker chips. One chip should be black (the jack), six another color, and six another color again.

Take turns positioning the jack by placing it on the table so that it overhangs the edge, pushing it sharply with the palm of the hand. Now take turns pushing your own buttons toward the jack in the same way, with the aim of ending up as close to the jack as possible.

After each round, one point goes to each of the six buttons nearest the jack. If a button falls off the table, score minus one, and if you make the jack fall off, score minus 5. The winner is the player with the most points after 5 games.

HAPPY NEW YEAR!

Answers

January 11: 1. butter; 2. rubble; 3. boat; 4. bubble; 5. best; 6. habit; 7. ball; 8. cob; 9. bite; 10. blanket.

January 22: poetry; rhythm; melody; chorus; comedy; priest; school; energy; magnet; church; amphitheater.

January 26: 1. silver birch; 2. yew (you); 3. cedar; 4. maple; 5. olive; 6. rowan; 7. elm.

February 4: amen, army, earl, early, earn, elan, lame, lane, layer, laymen, lean, learn, leman, lyre, male, mane, manly, manner, many, mare, marl, meal, meanly, name, namely, nary, near, nearly, rale, real, realm, ream, relay, rely, renal, yarn, yean, year, yearly, yearn.

February 15: 1. All work and no play makes *Jack* a dull boy. 2. A stitch in *time* saves nine. 3. Many hands make *light* work. 4. He laughs best who laughs *last*. 5. It is no use *crying* over spilt milk. 6. A *rolling* stone gathers no moss. 7. Here today, *gone* tomorrow. 8. Every *cloud* has a silver lining. 9. Actions speak louder than *words*. 10. Honesty is the best *policy*.

February 26: 1. Colorado; 2. California; 3. Oklahoma; 4. Nevada; 5. Montana; 6. Michigan; 7. South Carolina; 8. Rhode Island; 9. Maine.

March 9: 1. United States; 2. Britain; 3. New Zealand; 4. Canada; 5. Australia; 6. India; 7. France; 8. Spain; 9. South Africa; 10. U.S.S.R.

March 17: alee, alder, ameer, armed, dale, dame, dare, deal, dealer, dear, deem, deer, dele, deme, derm, dram, dream, eared, earl, elder, lade, lame, lard, leader, leer, made, male, mare, marl, mead, meal, medal, medlar, meed, mere, rale, real, reel, ream.

March 19: 1. red; 2. gold; 3. blue; 4. blue; 5. red;
6. golden; 7. black.

March 27: 1. exhale; 2. excuse; 3. exhaust; 4. explicit;
5. external; 6. exuberant; 7. exhibition; 8. expedite.

March 29: 1. Morocco; 2. India; 3. Norway; 4. Iceland;
5. Yugoslavia; 6. Zanzibar; 7. Thailand; 8. Ghana.

April 16: 1. A watched pot never boils.   2. A rolling stone
gathers no moss.   3. People in glass houses shouldn't throw
stones.   4. Familiarity breeds contempt.   5. It's the early
bird that catches the worm.   6. Absence makes the heart
grow fonder.   7. Too many cooks spoil the broth.   8. A stitch
in time saves nine.   9. Many hands make light work.
10. Half a loaf is better than none.   11. A miss is as good as
a mile.

April 18: 1. As you saiD, I AM ON Duty today.
(DIAMOND)   2. Please stOP ALl that noise. (OPAL)   3. Get
uP EARLy if you want to come too. (PEARL)   4. It is no use
shutting A GATE when the horse has bolted. (AGATE)
5. To make strawberry jAM, BERries and sugar are boiled
together. (AMBER)

April 23: 1G; 2F; 3H; 4E; 5D; 6B; 7C; 8A.

April 28: 1. advertisement; 2. baronet; 3. chemical,
chemist, chemistry; 4. diameter; 5. Greek; 6. Monsieur;
7. post meridian (after midday), post mortem (after death);
8. *répondez s'il vous plait* (please reply).

April 30: $50\frac{1}{2} + 49\frac{38}{76} = 100$

May 5: 1. wheelbarrow; 2. watering can; 3. flowerpot;
4. spade; 5. trowel; 6. lawnmower; 7. weed killer;
8. waterhose.

May 9: cheaper; swindle; tension; cowslip; indulge; pageant; addicts.

May 18: 1. ball; 2. umbrella; 3. door; 4. pencil; 5. fork; 6. stool; 7. coat.

May 24: 1. Charlotte Brontë; 2. Sam Clemens; 3. Eric Blair; 4. Mary Ann Evans; 5. Hector Munro; 6. Charles Dodgson.

June 12: a) Switch the plus sign and the equals sign. Then go around to the other side of the table and look at the numbers upside down. You will see ten equals one plus nine.   b) Switch the plus and equals signs to give eleven equals one plus ten.

June 23: aid, ail, also, daily, dais, daisy, dash, days, dial, dish, doily, hail, halo, hay, hod, hold, holy, idol, lad, lady, lash, lay, lido, lid, load, oil, oily, old, said, sail, say, shady, shoal, shod, slay, slid, soda, soil, sold, solid, soya.

June 28: 1. Rome; 2. Paris; 3. London; 4. Venice; 5. Paris; 6. Vienna; 7. Madrid; 8. Copenhagen.

July 4: 1. 1776; 2. John Adams; 3. Philadelphia; 4. Abraham Lincoln.

July 7: 1. snipe; 2. owls; 3. pheasants; 4. larks; 5. partridge; 6. geese; 7. goldfinches; 8. quails; 9. teal; 10. starlings.

July 23: 1. bitch; 2. nanny; 3. vixen; 4. mare; 5. doe; 6. pen; 7. ewe; 8. peahen.

July 28: a) 24; b) Jane is 44, Elizabeth is 33; c) 20.

August 10: 1. tame; 2. same; 3. sale; 4. male; 5. tale; 6. tape; 7. gape; 8. game; 9. fame; 10. fate; 11. date; 12. dace; 13. dice; 14. mice.

August 15: One O.

August 18: 1. swallow; 2. spangled; 3. cloak; 4. wing;
5. sign; 6. eye; 7. admiral; 8. clouded.

August 28: 1a. Norway, b. Austria, c. Peru;   2a. Japan, b.
Yugoslavia, c. Portugal;   3a. Italy, b. Germany, c. Greece;
4a. joining the Mediterranean and the Indian Ocean,
b. China, c. West Germany.

September 9: Arrange six straws on the table in the shape of
the letters NIL. The seventh straw can go anywhere you like,
for this is the one you take away.

September 13: 1. 12; 2. Libra, the scales; 3. Leo;
4. Aquarius, the water pourer, and Pisces, the fish;
5. Taurus, the bull; 6. Eight, if you count Sagittarius, the
centaur.

September 17: 1. France; 2. Denmark or Switzerland;
3. Netherlands; 4. Japan; 5. Sweden; 6. Italy.

October 6: 1. jackrabbit; 2. mouse; 3. racer; 4. mole;
5. swift; 6. chipmunk; 7. Meadow; 8. skunk; 9. bunting.
10. Eastern.

October 10: 1. apricot; 2. pineapple; 3. pear; 4. lemon;
5. elder. The initials spell APPLE.

October 22: 1. Mary, Mary, quite contrary, how does your
garden grow?   2. Baa, baa, black sheep, have you any
wool?   3. Hey diddle diddle, the cat and the fiddle, the cow
jumped over the moon.   4. Three blind mice, three blind
mice, see how they run, see how they run.   5. Little Jack
Horner sat in a corner eating his Christmas pie.   6. Mary had
a little lamb, its fleece was white as snow.   7. Little boy blue,
come blow your horn, the sheep's in the meadow, the cow's in
the corn.   8. Humpty Dumpty sat on a wall, Humpty Dumpty

had a great fall.   9. Old King Cole was a merry old soul and a merry old soul was he.   10. Sing a song of sixpence, a pocket full of rye.

October 23: fills, filly, fils, fishy, flows, foils, folly, fowl, hilly, holly, holy, howl, lily, lowly, oily, owlish, showy, sill, silly, silo, slowly, soil, swill, wholly, will, willy, wily, yowl.

November 4:
1. Running
2. Boxing
3. Soccer or Basketball
4. Fishing
5. Snooker (Pool)
6. Golf
7. Tennis
8. Rowing

November 8: 1. 10; 2. 10.

November 10: 1. Joe Greene is a football player, the rest are tennis players.   2. Steve Cauthen is a jockey, the rest are golfers.   3. Joe Frazier is a boxer, the rest are racing drivers.

November 13: 1. giant tortoise; 2. chameleon; 3. crocodile; 4. iguana; 5. basilisk; 6. gecko; 7. boa constrictor; 8. salamander.

November 29: eking, ergo, evoking, giro, given, gone, gore, govern, grin, groin, grove, ignore, inker, invoke, iron, kern, kine, king, kino, krone, ogive, ogre, oven, over, ovine, region, reign, rein, rink, rive, roving, vine, vireo.

December 5: Holly.

December 10:

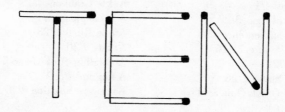

December 11: 1. Austria; 2. Belgium; 3. Switzerland; 4. Germany; 5. Egypt; 6. Liechtenstein; 7. Greece; 8. Hungary; 9. Israel; 10. Jamaica; 11. Cambodia; 12. Luxembourg; 13. Mexico; 14. Norway; 15. Poland; 16. Argentina; 17. Sweden; 18. Turkey; 19. Uruguay; 20. Vatican City; 21. Yugoslavia; 22. South Africa.

December 14: 1B; 2E; 3A; 4D; 5F; 6C.

December 20: 1. cats; 2. London; 3. 12; 4. December; 5. 2; 6. tobacco; 7. pigs; 8. ink.

December 22: inter, newt, rein, rent, rite, tern, tier, tire, twin, twine, went, weir, wine, wire, wren, writ, write.

December 27: A frog.

December 29: 1. Viola—the only stringed instrument. 2. Darts—not played with a ball. 3. Meringue—the only sweet food. 4. Pirouette—the name of a step, not a dance. 5. Mammal—this is not a specific breed. 6. Egypt—the word does not contain the letter *a*.

Index

Abbreviations 4/28
ABC Quiz 7/20
Acting Strangely 2/8
Action Painting 8/7
Act the Word 12/21
Agatha's Bell 2/5
Air, Earth and Water 5/14
All Change! 4/1
All Kinds of Eggs 3/27
Alphabetical Sentences 5/1
Alphabet Picture 11/16
Ambush 7/22
American States 2/26
Americas' Quick Quiz 5/11

Anagrams 6/15
Animal Carol 12/23
Animal Cries 3/14
Animal Emblems 3/9
Animal Portraits 7/6
Animal Races 9/1
Animals and Their Mates 7/23
Ankle Grabbers 7/12
Ant Language 1/1
Apple Rings 9/23
Artists 9/20
Australian Stick Game 5/30
Autograph 2/19
Backward Spelling 8/30

Badger 8/3
Balancing Contest 11/19
Balancing the Books 3/28
Ball-in-the-Box 8/2
Ball in the Net 12/9
Balloon Ball 3/24
Balloon Races 3/30
Bark Rubbings 1/30
Barricades 3/26
Beach Ball Races 7/30
Bears 4/14
Ben Hur 7/31
Beware Poison! 3/13
B-Gone 1/11
Birthday Lucky Numbers 2/12
Blind Balance 12/2
Blindfold Ballgame 6/17
Blindfold Stag 11/17
Blind Spider 5/2
Blind Tug 8/17
Blow Football 12/15
Blow It 7/16
Body Names 2/20
Book Relays 2/9
Bottle Cap Battle 5/22
Bowlorama 7/5
Brain-Teaser 4/30
Bridge Quiz 9/28
Broken Egg 6/26
Broomsticks 1/14
Burst the Bag 5/29
Buster 11/18
Busting the Tape 1/4
Butterflies and Moths 8/18
Button Game 11/21
Capture the Castle 8/5
Car Contest 6/19
Cart Horses 5/13
Catch! 3/21
Catch a Shooting Star 11/15
Catch the Balloon 8/21
Cat Game 2/7
Celebrities 12/25
Centipedes 3/2

Chalk Marks 2/3
Changing Trees 10/18
Cheat 5/31
Cheese Rollers 4/26
Chinese Boxing 6/8
Chinese Wrestling 5/10
Clattering Cans 7/25
Coin in the Bucket 11/7
Colditz 11/24
Collective Game 7/7
Colorful Songbirds 3/19
Colorful Thoughts 6/25
Compass Karen 4/22
Corko 8/6
Craftsman Kim 1/16
Crafty 2/16
Crazy Hockey 5/4
Cross Out the "A's" 12/30
Dart Boards 6/5
Desert Island 4/20
Dictionary Definitions 5/18
Dodg'em 3/11
Doggo 8/25
Dog in a Manger 2/23
Dog Show 12/28
Don't Say It 6/22
Down, Dog, Down 2/24
Ducks and Drakes 7/9
Easter Bonnet 4/12
Edison Game 2/11
"Emerald" Quiz 3/17
European Tour 6/28
Fall Collection 10/4
Famous Advertisements 12/13
Ferryman 6/10
Fetch 1/24
Fibber 10/20
Figure-Eight Race 2/13
Find the Matchbox 12/26
Find the Trees 1/26
Fingerprints 4/6
Fish Fingers 9/18
Floorball 9/8
Fly Around the World 8/16

Flying Flounder 10/27
Flying Plates 4/2
Flying Saucers 5/7
Follow On 7/3
Footprints 7/13
Fourteen All 1/15
Freeze 1/8
French Cricket 9/22
Friend or Foe? 9/3
From A to ZA 12/11
Fruit Names 9/7
Gem Smugglers 4/18
Ghostly Encounter 2/2
Ghosts 10/9
Goldfish 6/4
Gone Fishing 9/21
Googly Balloon 1/7
Grab! 7/21
Group Names 4/23
Guessing Games 1/9
Guess Their Ages 7/28
Hamburgers, Beans and
    French Fries 3/25
Happy New Year! 1/2
Hares and Hound 3/31
Hazards 9/9
Heave-Heave-Ho! 3/10
Hidden Fruit 10/10
Hidden Notes 4/16
Hidden Trees 4/15
High Dice, Low Dice 9/11
Hog Tie 6/3
Holidays 6/23
Hopball 11/14
Hopping and Charging 10/5
Hopping Relay 8/13
Hop, Step and Jump 9/2
Horse Feathers 9/24
Horses and Riders 6/16
Hot Shot 3/1
How Long Do They Live?
    12/14
How Many Coins? 3/23
How Many Notes? 1/23

How Many Shadows? 9/26
Human Parcel 1/10
Hunting Halloween 10/19
Independence Day Quiz 7/4
Indian Bowls 1/28
Indian Leg Wrestling 10/15
Indian Pistol 8/4
Indoor Frenchie 7/14
Instant Names 7/1
Island Shapes 1/11
I Went Shopping 4/10
Joggers 9/25
Journey of Terror 4/11
Jousting 4/27
Jumbled Names 5/5
Jumping Johnny 2/29
J-U-N-E 6/1
Kick Stick 4/4
Knee Relays 4/29
Ladies' Night 9/29
Legpull 8/31
Lie Detector 2/17
Listening Post 11/12
List of Firsts 4/21
Loaded Dice? 9/27
Lobster Pot 8/26
Longest Words 7/11
Lost Person 3/12
Magic Arm 4/17
Magic Carpet 7/18
Magic Pepper 11/22
Mailmen 2/25
Main Street Quiz 10/7
Manhattan Golf 9/12
"Mannerly" Quiz 2/4
Match Box 8/12
Math Genius? 9/15
Memory Circles 7/19
Memory Game 3/16
Metallic Names 3/3
Mind Reading 5/26
Missing Adjectives 11/9
Missing Six 8/29
Mixed Questions 12/20

Modern Nursery Rhymes 4/3
Monster Problems 11/8
Monsters 10/30
Musical Chairs 12/16
Musical Numbers 1/21
Mystery Tapes 12/7
Mystery Ten 6/12
Name that Man! 9/10
Name the Girl 8/9
National Flags 9/17
Nature Quiz 9/14
Newsreader 3/20
Niagara 6/30
Nosey 4/19
Numbers, Numbers 7/15
Number Story 10/2
Nursery Rhyme Quiz 10/22
Odd Man Out 12/29
Odd One Out 11/10
Ologies 10/1
One Letter at a Time 8/10
Operation 2/22
Over the Shoulder 11/3
Pairs 2/10
Pancake Contest 2/27
Pandemonium 8/1
Party Chains 12/12
Pass the Matchbox 5/20
Pass the Orange 6/21
Pass the—What? 12/24
Patience in Fours 12/18
Patience in Pairs 5/16
Pen Names 5/23
Pick Up Sticks 10/14
Plate Spinning 5/21
Plow Horses 11/1
Pot Black 11/2
Proverbial Problem 8/15
Proverbs 2/15
Push of War 5/25
Push the Button 12/31
Push the Cork 1/5
Puzzling Poem 12/5
Quarter Staffs 2/6

Queenie 9/19
Quiz for Travelers 8/28
Raft Game 4/9
Railroad Tunnel 9/4
Red Hot Poker 10/17
Reptiles Quiz 11/13
"Revoking" Quiz 11/29
Rhyming Story 6/11
Rice Trailing 5/27
Riding the Trains 1/31
Ring the Bottle 9/5
Rise and Shine! 4/13
Rocks and Rapids 9/30
Rolling Along 5/19
Rope Horseshoes 5/6
Run for Your Life 4/25
Running the Gauntlet 3/8
RUOK? 10/12
Sand Cartoons 8/11
Say It! 8/20
Scavenger Hunt 8/27
Scissors, Paper, Stone 10/28
Scrumping 10/21
Seek the Sevens 5/9
Seven Match Trick 5/17
Shadow Play 1/19
Shadows on the Wall 8/23
Shapes and Things 6/20
Shipwrecked 8/19
Shoes for All 12/3
Side by Side 3/18
Silent Letter 11/11
Silhouette Portraits 5/12
Simon Says 7/2
Skipping Games 1/25
Sleeping Indian 11/30
Sleeping Pirate 6/24
Slippery Soap 12/4
Snake Game 7/24
Snow Castle 1/18
Snow People 1/6
Snow Snake 12/17
Sort Out the News 9/6
Sounds Game 12/19

Spirits 10/31
Split Words 1/22
Spongy 7/17
Sports Jargon 11/4
Spotters 6/6
Sprint Tug-of-War 5/3
Sprouts 3/4
Stamp Collector 5/23
Statues 11/26
Stepping Stones 11/25
Stone Age 4/5
Straight Face 3/7
Strange Countries 3/29
String Along 6/27
String Game 7/8
Stump Speeches 12/6
Suspension Game 11/5
Swipe 12/1
Table Ball 6/13
Table Tennis Relay 2/1
Taboo 3/15
Tailwaggers 10/11
Take a Card 2/18
Talking Pictures 2/21
Tap-Tap-Tap 11/23
Tap the Balloon 10/26
Taste Buds 10/8
Team Chariots 7/10
Telegrams 10/16
Telephone Numbers 1/12
Ten! 12/10
Ten Ton Fingers 7/27
Three-Way Tug 4/8
Throw the Dice 10/25
Thud and Blunder 1/29
Tick-Tock 11/20
Tin Can Shy 1/3
Total Surrender 6/2
Touch Game 1/20

Trade Names 11/28
Tramps' Race 4/24
Trapball 11/27
Travel Game 5/8
Treasure Map 4/7
Tripod Football 1/13
Tub Ball 7/29
Tug of War 7/26
Tune Tapping 5/28
T.V. Stars 6/14
Umbrella Obstacles 11/6
Valentino 2/24
Volley Balloon 3/5
Wet Day Race 6/29
What Am I? 6/9
What Rhyme This Time?
    10/24
What Tree Am I? 12/8
Wheelbarrow 5/15
When We Were Young . . .
    2/28
Which Leaf? 6/18
Who Am I? 12/27
Who'll Get There First? 3/22
Whose Walk? 10/3
Who's Ticklish? 8/24
Wildlife Quiz—Prairies 10/6
Wildlife Silhouettes 8/14
Winter 12/22
Witch's Broom 10/13
Wolfish Word Game 10/23
Wolf, Wolf . . . 1/27
Word-Making 8/22
Wrist Wrestlers 10/29
Wristy 3/6
X Marks the Spot 6/7
Yawning 9/16
Your Move Next 8/8
Zodiac Quiz 9/13